A FUNNY THING HAPPENED TO THE CHURCH

A FUNNY THING HAPPENED TO THE CHURCH

HUMOR, CARTOONS, SATIRE and FICTION

from the pages of THE CRITIC

Edited by

Joel Wells

The Macmillan Company
Collier-Macmillan Ltd., London

Library of Congress Catalog Card Number: 71-76587

FIRST PRINTING

The Macmillan Company
Collier-Macmillan Canada Ltd., Toronto, Ontario

Printed in the United States of America

CONTENTS

INTRODUCTION

A CASE CAN be made, I suggest, that there is an antipathy between humor and believers. The phrase, "takes religion seriously," applies not only to Puritans but to most everyone who is religiously aware. The evidence to support this thesis can be found without research. If Catholics possessed a well-developed sense of humor, would they have long put up with Cardinals Spellman, O'Boyle and McIntyre? Or with the Roman Curia? Or with the whole array of anachronistic customs such as ring-kissing, clergy draped in feminine accouterments, and high-falutin' forms of address (Your Eminence, Your Excellency, Most Reverend, Right Reverend and Very Reverend)? If Jews were susceptible to hilarity, would they pay attention to the Jerusalem Rabbinical Council's campaign to prevent smoking, the use of electricity, or even the signing of a restaurant check on the Sabbath? If Protestants could laugh at themselves, would they tolerate the POAU (or whatever it is called in the enlightened sixties), Dr. Norman Vincent Peale or the Reverend Malcolm Boyd?

As any editor can tell you, you can probably get away with heresy, libel or obscenity in these days of freedom and love, but beware the wisecrack or the satirical jibe. If, for example, you see nothing structure-shaking in Martin Murphy's playful portraits of the "new" nun to be found elsewhere in these pages, your sense of what is proper and fitting is badly underdeveloped. No feature in the almost three decades of *The Critic*'s existence brought forth a comparable response. A deluge of letters, all vituperative, poured in from nuns young and old, liberal and conservative, pious and worldly, loving and mean, intellectual and domestic—all united in denouncing poor Mr. Murphy and the editor, as well as their forebears and their four-footed descendants. There was hell to pay, if you will pardon the old-fashioned reference.

On the other hand, you can make an even stronger case in arguing that humor is rapidly disappearing from all American life. Even the dirty jokes aren't funny any more. If *Playboy* cartoons are representative of our wit, Americans are indeed a miserable people. It may even be that the sole source of humor today comes from religious liberals. Harvey Cox, now that his Secular City balloon has deflated, seems about to launch a whole theological movement based on joy. And a group of Catholic liturgists convened in Washington for the sole purpose, so it seemed, of displaying buttons reading "Damn everything but the circus." At least they were trying.

But enough of the trivial. What you want to know—what alert readers of *The Critic* have always wanted to know—is whether there really is a Joel Wells. I am happy to inform you that he does exist. And a finer specimen of American boyhood you could never find in Daleyland. Lean, bronzed, taut-muscled, crew-haired; vigorous, warm, charming, jovial; loving, generous, zealous, committed. That is Joel Wells as he sees himself. In fairness, I must admit that his friends and colleagues and, I suspect, his family do not necessarily share that view. To prepare this white paper, I surveyed those who might be expected to know the real Joel Wells and begged for a word or a phrase that might best characterize this late-flowering genius. Among the printable data furnished me are: churlish, cynical, bilious, grouty, surly, sullen, waspish, crusty, pinch-penny, contentious, bawdy—all of which fortunately are qualities that have traditionally been associated with the rare breed of humorist. My well-known devotion to charity as well as my own vulnerability prevents me from offering you an accurate physical description of this artist with the scalpel except to note that although he is a well-known lecturer, it is a painful fact that he has never been sought for a return engagement.

But this, unlike most introductions, is supposed to be functional. The purpose: to justify the editor of this choice collection for seeing fit, in all modesty, to include six of his own parodies. This is not easy to explain. Granted they are damn funny, that they have been widely reprinted in the religious and the general press and that there are enough Xerox copies of any one of them floating around to equal the words of a *National Catholic Reporter* editorial or a pastoral letter from the American Bishops. Granted, too, that he didn't have to pay himself royalties and that his publisher urged him to include these minor classics. The fact remains, it does seem pushy of him.

I must add that the cartoons, short stories, parodies and other humorous writings in this book are the fruit of Mr. Wells' four exciting years as editor of *The Critic*. In this brief time the circulation of the magazine has tripled—we estimate that today .0007 of all American Catholics find *The Critic* almost indispensable. To sum up, he is a brilliant editor, a scintillating and talented humorist and a treasured friend. This book is worthy of him.

DAN HERR

A FUNNY THING HAPPENED TO THE CHURCH

1. THE FIRST PAPAL PRESS CONFERENCE*

by Andrew M. Greeley

KEVIN CARDINAL ORSINI was elected pope by "inspiration" on the forty-third day of the conclave; ninety-six-year-old Cardinal Antonelli leaped from his throne in the Sistine chapel and shouted in his feeble voice, "Orsini Papa!" With varying degrees of weariness, surprise, dismay and joy, all the other cardinals echoed the shout—"Orsini Papa!" It was then pointed out by several of those present that this was indeed a legitimate and definitive way of selecting a pope, even though it was one that apparently had not been used in the history of the Papacy. Almost without realizing it, the cardinals had selected their youngest member, the forty-six-year-old Orsini, as the new pope. There were some, later on, who claimed that Antonelli had been sound asleep and in his sleep had a nightmare of Orsini becoming pope. His cry of "Orsini Papa!" it was alleged, was not an inspiration from the Holy Spirit, but the result of a bad dream. In any case, Orsini's supporters had seized the opportunity to proclaim their man the victor, and after forty-three days of a conclave in which nine cardinals had already died, no one was prepared to dispute his claim to the Papacy.

* From the February–March 1969 issue of *The Critic*.

In his first act as pope, Orsini, now known as Kevin the First, giving the traditional blessing, *Urbi et Orbi*, in a black business suit and tie, had announced that, while he had deep respect for the College of Cardinals, and had every intention of continuing it as an important arm of the Church, he thought it would be inappropriate, under the circumstances of the modern world, to continue the College as the Papal electoral body. He announced that henceforth the pope would be elected by all the archbishops of the world. "Unless," he added, "my colleagues in the Synod can come up with a better idea."

The day after his election, Orsini announced the first English language Papal press conference. Before the Pontiff arrived in the banquet room of the Rome Filton, where the conference was to take place, members of the Vatican press corps compared notes on the very strange background of Kevin the First. His parents were Prince Raphael Orsini, now a member of the Italian Senate, and Princess Annie (nee O'Brien) Orsini, a Dublin actress whom Prince Raphael had wooed and wed while he was the third secretary of the Italian mission to Dublin. Their son had been raised in the Flatbush area of Brooklyn while Prince Raphael was on the staff of the United Nations, and he had attended Fordham University and the Harvard Graduate School of Business before beginning his theological studies at the Pontifical Gregorian University. His rise in the Papal diplomatic service had been meteoric, but his reputation for pragmatism, liberalism and a somewhat off-beat sense of humor, as well as the fact that he spoke both Italian and English with a Brooklyn accent, had made him an unlikely candidate for the Papacy.

Kevin the First, attired in a gray Seville Row suit, light blue shirt and paisley tie, finally arrived at the Monte Mario for his press conference, a transcript of which appeared the following day in *The New York Times*.

Q. (Times of London) *Your Holiness, the whole world is wondering—*

A. Please don't call me Your Holiness. I don't know that I'm all that holy and it's sort of an old-fashioned name. You can call me Pope or Mr. Pope, but please don't call me Your Holiness.

Q. *Well, yes, Sir. The whole world is wondering what your position will be on the birth control issue.*

A. I think it's a very complex issue and one that I certainly wouldn't want to address myself to in any specific detail this morning. We have really messed up this sex business in the Church for a long time and I don't think we're going to be able to make any coherent Christian statement on family planning until we do a lot of thinking and talking about the whole question of sexual personalism. I'm going to summon the Synod of Bishops into session the week after next, and certainly one of the top items on my agenda will be to ask my colleagues if they will set up a commission to consider a statement on the meaning of sex in the Christian tradition.

Q. (Chicago Sun-Times) *Do we understand, then, Mr. Pope, that you intend to convene the Synod of Bishops at once?*

A. Why yes, of course I do. This is an extremely difficult job I've been saddled with and I certainly don't intend to try and do it all myself. What's the point of having all these bishops throughout the world unless they're going to bear some of the responsibility? I'm going to have them in session for a couple of months every year for the rest of my administration, and they may as well resign themselves to buying commuter tickets to Rome.

Q. (Times of London) *But, Sir, if I understand you correctly, there is going to be some considerable delay before you address yourself to the birth control issue. In the meantime, aren't you afraid that most Catholic couples will continue to consider artificial contraception a mortal sin?*

A. No, I don't think so. If they do think it's a mortal sin, they are, in my judgment, wrong, but I'm certainly not going to try and impose my views on their conscience—at least not until I have been advised by my colleague bishops.

Q. (St. Louis Post-Dispatch) *There has been considerable talk of restoring the practice of popular election of bishops to the Catholic Church. Would you care to comment on this possibility?*

A. Oh, I'd be happy to comment. Two of my predecessors of happy memory—I can't quite remember what their names were, but they were back in the sixth century—said that it was sinful to choose a bishop by any other method besides popular election. Being at heart a very conservative fellow, I agree with them, so I'm going to do everything in my power to sell the Synod of Bishops on restoring popular election as soon as we can. It may take a bit of selling, but when they see how tough the job is going to be in my administration, I think a lot of them are going to be only too happy to have a successor in four or five years.

Q. (St. Louis Post-Dispatch) *Then am I to understand, Sir, that you are in favor of limited terms for bishops and perhaps even for the pope?*

A. Well, if you think I'm going to stay in this office until I die, you're sadly mistaken. This may be a fine job for five or ten years, but after that I'm going to want to retire someplace where it's peaceful and quiet. It doesn't seem to me to be fair to ask anybody to hold a major leadership position for more than five, or ten years, at the most. I assume that when the Synod of Bishops ponders this matter at some length, they will agree with me.

Q. (New York Times) *Have you made any decisions about the selection of a Papal cabinet?*

A. That's a very good question, Scotty, and I'm not sure that I can give a complete answer, but at least I have some ideas. Sister Mary Luke is going to be made Secretary of the Congregation of the Religious, and Barbara Ward, Secretary of the Congregation of the Laity. I also am going to ask Bishop Butler if he'll head up a new office combining all our relationships with other religions, and I think Cardinal Suenens will make a great Secretary of State, if I can ever persuade him to leave

Belgium. Also we're going to need a man like Cardinal Cody to straighten out the financial mess around here. Beyond that, I am consulting with some of my closest advisors to find out what other talent is available that we might be able to recruit to serve in the cabinet. I hope to have more specific announcements in a week or two, but you've got to realize that this whole thing has taken me somewhat by surprise.

Q. (Wall Street Journal) *Are we to take it, Sir, that you are going to make public the financial status of the Vatican?*

A. Well, I'm going to try to do it as soon as I can figure out what the financial status is. As far as I can understand, nobody but God exactly understands the finances of the Vatican, and unfortunately he's not about to make a private revelation on the subject.

Q. (Triumph) *Most Holy Father—*

A. I'm not Holy, and I'm certainly not Most Holy, and I'm also certainly not your father or anybody else's, so call me Pope, or Mr. Pope, or Bishop, and drop the rest of that nonsense.

Q. (Triumph, *again*) *You will, of course, maintain the Papal diplomatic service?*

A. I will most certainly do no such thing. The only reason we ever had diplomatic service in the first place was that communications weren't very good and they had to have somebody on the scene who could make decisions in the name of the Papacy. Given the kind of communication we have now, the diplomatic service is obsolescent, so it seems to me that the first thing we do is to transfer all the powers of the nuncios or the apostolic delegates to the National Conference of Bishops. Then they should send representatives to Rome to deal with the central offices here. There's no point in running the Church as though the jet airplane and the radio-telephone hadn't been invented.

Q. (National Catholic Reporter) *What contribution, if any, do you think the lay people have to make to the life of the Church?*

A. What contribution, if any? Well that's kind of a silly question; they don't have any *contribution* to make—they *are* the Church.

Without them we might just as well fold up our tents and steal away into the hills, if only because without them nobody is going to pay to keep the organization going. As a matter of fact, given the way we've treated the lay people for so long, I am surprised that they have paid as much as they have to keep us going. We shouldn't make any major decisions, it seems to me, until the implications of these decisions have been kicked around at the grass roots and we've got the reaction of the rank and file membership to what's going on. So we've got to have an assembly of the lay people of the parish and of the diocese and of the national Churches, and then finally, of the international Church. As soon as we can possibly get this sort of thing set up, we're going to do it. The trouble is that we can't do it overnight, so we're going to have to limp along for a while without having the advantage of grass roots participation. But one of the first things I intend to toss into the laps of my colleagues when I get together with the Synod is the problem of how we can most quickly get an international network of lay senates established. If we don't have them, we are certainly going to make the Holy Spirit work overtime.

Q. (Los Angeles Times) *Do you expect, Sir, that there is going to be much change in the canon law in the near future?*

A. You better believe there's going to be changes. I have the highest respect for the code of canon law; it is one of the greatest legal masterpieces of all time, and that's why I think we must let it be a *living* masterpiece and evolve into something that's even more perfect than itself. Of course its evolution is going to be rather dramatic, I think, in years to come, because very clearly what we need is some sort of international constitution which sets down general principles and, particularly, general rights and freedoms, and then lets the local hierarchies worry about legislating to meet their own problems.

Q. (St. Louis Post-Dispatch) *Do you expect to separate the legislative and judicial functions of the Church?*

A. Oh, you almost have to do that, if you're going to keep everybody honest. It seems to me that we ought to turn the Roman

Rota into a kind of supreme court of the Church to which people can appeal when they feel that their rights have been violated by the lower courts; and the exact shape of the lower courts should be determined by each national hierarchy. Given the complexity of the world today, it would be a terrible burden on the Roman judges to expect them to understand the problems that come in from every country, so they really should only have to hear the most important kind of appellate cases.

Q. (Detroit Free Press) *Does that mean, Sir, that you intend to have a reform of marriage legislation?*

A. I almost wish you hadn't asked that, because that's one of the most fouled-up problems that we have to face. I've already got some of my staff working on temporary changes that are going to improve the methods we're already using. I certainly hope that somebody in the Synod of Bishops has a brilliant idea of how we can straighten the mess out permanently, but I, for one, am at a loss as to how to do it. Nevertheless, I think we ought to get out of the divorce trial business. It just seems to me that the Church would have been better off long ago if all the people we've trained to be canon lawyers had been trained to be counseling psychologists instead.

Q. (Le Figaro *of Paris*) *Do you plan, Sir, to have any more Papal trips?*

A. Well, I like to travel as much as the next man, and maybe even a little more. But it seems to me that traveling is more of a vacation than anything else, and I don't expect to learn much on my trips. If the national hierarchies elect good leaders, I presume they'll be the ones who will keep me informed on what's going on, but it seems to me that the Papal trip really is pretty much a waste of time. Just the same, let me assure you I'm not going to spend the rest of my term in Rome.

Q. (The Guardian, *Manchester, England*) *What do you intend to do about* L'Osservatore Romano?

A. I wish to heaven I knew what to do about it—would you like to be editor of it?

Q. *No, Sir, I wouldn't.*

A. Yeah, that's what they all say. Next question, please.

Q. (New Orleans Time-Picayune) *What is your position on the celibacy question?*

A. Well, it's pretty clear we've got to do something about it, though I don't want to be stampeded into it until we give the Synod and the various priest and lay senates around the world the time to talk about it. I think we ought to make it easy for people to get out of the priesthood when they want to with the promise that, if we do decide to have a married priesthood, we'll give them the option of getting back in—although I think we're going to want to take the option of not letting them back in under some circumstances. You know, every once in a while I'm inclined to think we should let anybody leave the priesthood who wants to, just so long as they and the women they're going to marry are ready to undergo a year of psychotherapy. But I don't suppose you could impose that any more—that might be too autocratic. Just the same, it might be nice if we made the therapy available for them; we would also probably run out of psychiatrists.

Q. (Frankfurter Allegemeine Zeitung) *Do you expect there to be any heresy trials in your administration?*

A. Good God, no!

Q. (Frankfurter Allegemeine Zeitung) *But what is your opinion of heresy?*

A. Well, I don't know that I can find much trace in the Bible of the idea that there was such a thing as heresy—it seems to me to be an idea that came along much later on, and I wonder if we might not be well-advised to put it aside. I think there may be some theologians who speak a little beyond what the consciousness of the Church's own message would be able to permit, at the present time; but I'd much prefer to handle this by having a board of theologians sit down and discuss the matter with the theologian who seems to have gone beyond the consciousness and see whether it can be worked out—see whether he really can say the things he says and still, at least at the present time, be part of us. But the idea of excommunicating people and labeling them heretics seems to me to be terribly old-fashioned.

Q. (Frankfurter Allegemeine Zeitung) *But what do you think of the case of Reverend Dr. Hans Küng?*

A. You mean do I think Hans is a heretic? Why don't be silly. Hans is basically a conservative. I never could understand why people thought he was dangerous or a radical. How in the world can anybody who owns a Mercedes-Benz be a radical?

Q. (Il Messaggero *of Rome*) *What, your Holiness—I mean, Pope —what is your opinion on the forthcoming Italian elections?*

A. I hope everybody votes in them.

Q. (Il Messaggero) *But what party are you supporting?*

A. We've got a secret ballot in this country just like most other countries and who I vote for is my secret.

Q. (Il Messaggero) *But are you going to take a stand in Italian politics?*

A. What's the matter? Do you think I'm crazy?

Q. (Il Messaggero) *Does this mean, then, that the Vatican is assuming a policy of non-intervention in Italian politics?*

A. You bet your life it does.

Q. (Milwaukee Sentinel) *Do you intend, Sir, to continue the practice of censorship of books that are written by Catholics?*

A. I think it would be a good idea to take every imprimatur in the world and throw it in the furnace, and we ought to throw half of the book censors in the furnace too. The basic thing to say about censorship is that it didn't work, it doesn't work, and it's never going to work, and the quicker we forget about it, the better off we're all going to be.

Q. (The Washington Post) *From all you've said so far, Sir, it would seem that you are really anticipating a very notable decline in Papal authority. I wonder if you could tell us whether you think that this is a drastic change in Church doctrine?*

A. Well, I don't know where you got that idea; I must say, as a matter of fact, I think what I'm talking about is a rather notable increase in Papal authority. A pope who is informed by his colleagues in the Synod and by the lay people of the world and a network of lay associations, who has had for his advisors the best theologians and scholars in the world, who makes informed decisions and can rely on cooperation with these decisions, isn't exactly a weak leader. On the contrary, I think he's a pretty strong one. It's not my intention to weaken the powers of the Papacy at all, but to strengthen the powers of the Papacy; and the reforms that I've discussed are designed to do just that. I might also say that it's probably going to increase the work of the Papacy and that's why I don't intend to spend much more than five or ten years in the office. You know it's kind of easy to make unilateral decisions, but it's awfully hard to gain consensus.

Q. (Philadelphia Inquirer) *Do you mean, then, that you view the Papacy as being essentially a role of one who presides over a consensus?*

A. Well, it depends on what you mean by presides. If you mean do I just sit back and wait until everybody's ideas come in and then coordinate them, I can assure you that's not how I intend to play the part. Nor do I see myself as providing the answers to questions. It seems to me that the most important job of a man in my position is not to answer questions, but to ask them; not to supply people with answers, but to challenge them to find out what the answers are. That's going to be a pretty tough job and I'm going to have to gather some of the best minds in the world around me if I'm going to be able to pull it off.

Q. (NBC News) *Do you think, Sir, that your job as Sovereign Pontiff is going to be a difficult one?*

A. Sovereign Pontiff! The trouble with you, Chet, is that you've been reading *L'Osservatore Romano* too much. Sure, it's going to be a difficult job. Any top level administrative job is difficult, but if you surround yourself with a good staff and make sure the channels of communication are open, it's not an impossible job. As I say, I think ten years is plenty in it, but I'm rather looking forward to it.

Q. (Le Monde) *What do you think about the conflict between science and religion?*

A. I don't think there is one, and if there has been one, we'll now put a stop to it.

Q. (CBS News) *Do you have any opinion, Sir, on the question of the emerging nations?*

A. Well, I'm certainly going to support the encyclicals on the subject written by my predecessors, though I don't think I'm going to issue any new encyclicals—as a matter of fact, I think we probably ought to declare a moratorium on encyclical writing. I'm going to wait until we get the Synod together and see what my colleagues from these nations think would be the best policy for the Church to assume in the matter. Given the immense number of people that we have in many of these nations, it seems to me that we ought to be doing a much better job than we are. I have a hunch that there might be something wrong with the leadership the Church is providing in the new nations, and if there is, you can believe that there's going to be a real shakeup.

Q. (Miami Herald) *Do you think the religious life of the priests and brothers and sisters is going to survive?*

A. It's not going to survive unless a lot of religious communities get a move on and take themselves out of the Middle Ages. Those who are willing to modernize, democratize, and treat the members like human beings, I think have a great future ahead of them. This is a day when everybody is crying for community, and a good religious order should be able to provide more community than anything else. But my personal opinion is that a lot of them are so bad that they simply are beyond redemption. That's one of the problems that my colleagues in the Synod are going to have to work out, too.

You know, there's something I'd like to say to you fellows. These questions have all been pretty good, but they're mostly on the internal problems of the Church. I suppose I can understand why you'd ask them, because most of the news the Church has made in the last couple hundred years has had to do with internal problems. We were bogged down for so long in ancient morbid structures that I guess the modernization of these structures was news. But I think I can tell you that by a year from now, or two years at the most, we're going to be so modernized that all you'll be able to ask me will be substantive questions, like What has the Church got to say about the meaning of human love? or What does it have to say about the quest for freedom? or What does it have to say about life and death? What does it have to say about getting old? or about leisure? or about the mass media? I'm kind of glad you're not asking me those questions now, because I haven't the faintest idea what the answers are, and I can't even promise that I'll have very good answers a year from now, but they're going to be better than the present ones. Any more questions?

Q. (Seventeen) *Do you have anything to say for young people?*

A. Well, I'd say to the young to be patient with us older people because we're going to try to learn how to listen to you, and that we'll try, in our turn, to be patient with you while you try to learn how to listen to us. I don't think there's much wrong with young people that a little bit of experience won't cure— and there's not much wrong with older people that sharing the enthusiasm of the young won't cure.

Q. (New York Times) *Thank you, Mr. Pope.*

A. You're quite welcome, Scotty.

2. *A MICROMANUAL FOR THE UNDERGROUND CHURCH**

Compiled from approved sources by Richard Mann

> Dedicated to the sad,
> searching millions
> who until now have
> not known the way to
> the glittering ghetto.

Acknowledgments

The compiler wishes to express his deepest gratitude to all those ineffably faithful and generous souls employed in the Secret Archives of the major American Dioceses who at no moment hesitated to provide him with classified documents, sweet words and unfeigned sympathy.

It would be more than invidious not to mention, too, the help received from the Library of Congress, the Bibliothèque National, the British Museum, the Museum of Modern Art, and Tiger Morse.

Among those who provided unpublished retreat notes, home liturgies, old clippings, petitions, posters, and sundry invaluable scraps, I must mention here: the literary executors for Evelyn

* From the February–March 1969 issue of *The Critic*.

Waugh, Suzy Knickerbocker, Thomas Hoving, Martin Darcy, S.J., Tallulah Bankhead, Cardinal McIntyre, Andy Warhol, Julia Child, William F. Buckley Jr., Twiggy, Three Swamis, The Mothers of Invention, Norman Mailer, Mao, Princess Ira von Furstenberg, Danny the Red, the Center for the Study of Democratic Institutions, The Doors, Everett Dirksen, Truman Capote, Padre Pio, Eugenia Sheppard, the Editors of Time, Inc., Betty Furness, Warren Beatty, Great Books, Inc., Mia Farrow, Charles Atlas, the McLuhan people and Miss Mae West.

Contents

Chapter 1: Definition of the Underground Church

We must commence with an anguished apology. It was intended that this space be occupied by a Non-Verbal Presentation created especially for the Micromanual by Sister Coeur de Lion. Unfortunately for us all, Sister is maximally involved in a Multi-Mixed-Media-Happening-Environment-Sensitivity-Awareness-Session, the termination of which has yet to be announced.

Accordingly we reluctantly proffer the following linear and grotesquely Gutenbergian definition, description, thrust, or what have you. It has pleased us to cast it in catechism form for easy memorization.

Q. *What is the Underground Church?*

A. I don't like your tone. You must sound more reverential than that.

Q. *Please, as one lost in the mists of irrelevancy, over-structuralization and top-heavy, hierarchical juridicism, unveil to me the features which I but now sense of the Underground Church.*
A. (solemnly but with increasing excitement bordering on enthusiasm) The Underground Church is what IS, really With It, Relevant, Prophetical, as Charismatic Response to and of the Pneuma to and with the Contemporary Now-Situation, in such way as to postulate Radical, Grass-Roots, Being-with-the-Secular Involvement where the Present Position and Horizon finds Its Self in Estrangement and Alienation, Engaged with Powers and Principalities in the never-ending, always to be projected Salvation Eventuality.
Q. *How delightful!*
A. You're welcome.

Chapter 2: Handy Guide for Arriving at Your Own Theology

No one can afford to be without their own theology. Those who have already memorized the preceding chapter may, naturally, dispense with this one and go on to Chapter 3 which is, as it were, the cornerstone, hub and very summit of the Micromanual. However, since we can never have too much of a good thing, and also because there are some in whom the post-Tridentine Baroque spirit of elaboration dies hard, we proffer here the following information and experience-tested tactics.

A theology is like a pet. It is nice to have around, fun for the children but messy if not house-broken, and must be kept in its place. One should never become involved in a theology, especially if it belongs to someone else.

It will save a lot of heartbreak, inferiority feelings and unadorned bad temper if one will but memorize the following: EVERY THEOLOGY IS *SOMEONE'S* THEOLOGY. No properly brought-up person will take a dialogue beyond the point of your saying: "But that's only your *theology*." You can then get back to concentrating on finding what there is left to drink. Many arguments are avoided this way, and if your friends are of the sort who would take the dialogue beyond that point, then they are definitely not gentlemen.

The following maxims, if properly memorized, will be of sterling service in your speedy, not to say instant, developing of the theology which best suits the real twentieth-century You.

1. Theology springs from Life.
2. Theology is essentially Political.
3. The True Theologian is one of the Truly Beautiful People.
4. All Truly Beautiful People are really Theologians.
5. Theology cannot be found in Books.
6. Theology cannot be found in Thoughts.
7. We don't know for sure if Theology can be found in Drugs.
8. All European movie Directors are really Theologians.
9. The Real Theology comes out of slums.
10. The Doing of Theology (e.g. sending a donation to the local ghetto) can be tax deductible.

Chapter 3: How to Furnish Your Living Room

As was pointed out earlier, this chapter is the cornerstone, etc., and must be memorized in its profound entirety.

The living room is an extension of one's personality, a stage set for the soul, the indispensable environmental equipage for authentic encounter and never-to-be-disdained dialogue.

You will be immediately and definitively recognized as IN or OUT by what you have in your living room. (Bathrooms have a minor, though real, significance; of this, more later.) It is most important that you display the correct household gods, and so the following list has been compiled in order that you might, with ease and moderate expense, appear before the Right People, shameless, unafraid and trembling with delight, as an out-and-out member of the Underground Church.

OF ABSOLUTE NECESSITY

1. Lie, starve, grovel, fight, steal (even pay money) in order to obtain an original print by Corita Kent. This is the Great Sign, your Authenticating Seal. Naturally the bigger are the better, but if you can't get a really large one, settle for a small; frame it with a wide, wide frame and train a light on it. The picture should be hung alone and majestic on your largest white living room wall. If the picture is visible, in whole or in part, from the entrance hall, then you are definitely on the way to making it big.

Reproductions of prints, cut out of magazines, are scarcely to be recommended, but if this is all, after a sincere and tireless effort, you are able to come by, then frame one in the most elaborate manner possible and cover it with plate glass which will reflect any and all light. You won't fool the really IN people who know the prints by heart, so keep up the quest for the really real.

2. On the coffee table you must have the dust jackets from the latest books by the Berrigan Brothers. Just about everyone really IN the Underground Church works in or knows someone in the publishing business. Prevail upon an Underground friend to bring a few jackets home from work. If you are still in the process of arriving, steal several jackets from your local library or book-seller. Reading is definitely superfluous in the Underground Church (one must skim reviews, though), and so no one is likely to look inside the jackets. They can be filled out with an old stocking box or a few copies of *TV Guide*. If someone has presented you with the entire book, resist the urge to forge an inscription from the author, unless you have heard a few anecdotes concerning him which have not yet made the rounds. These, when related to a hushed group, will be a sign of the inscription's authenticity.

OF SECONDARY NECESSITY

1. Incense. Sticks burn better than blocks. Don't settle for a mundane scent such as pine or California cherry, but be radical

and seek out the exotic fragrances. If you are sufficiently liberated psychologically from the Established Church so that the incense sold in church stores does not activate traumatic memories, then ordinary "Benediction" incense will usually be found to be quite delightful. Be thoughtful of your guests, however; you may induce in people not as well adjusted as yourself an irresistible impulse to sing the *"Tantum Ergo."* If this happens, smile.

2. A metal or plastic Buddha will demonstrate your breadth of spirit and genuine openmindedness. A flower may be placed before it.

3. Have a few strings of beads (old rosaries with the chain removed are indistinguishable from the better hippie beads) laying around. Guests like to play with these and even put them on as the evening progresses.

4. Small menorahs were IN quite recently and, at the moment of writing, may not be completely OUT.

5. Try to get a second-hand, inexpensive guitar. There is not the slightest need for you to know how to play it (no one is likely to stop talking long enough to listen), but it does make a relevant decoration for a corner.

6. DON'T have any icons. They are very definitely OUT and enormously sectarian.

7. A few stones with writing on them (quotes from the Real People) may be placed here and there. If the only stones you can obtain are too small for more than a couple of words, then paint a simple daisy on them.

8. Banners. A large banner with a text is a very important status symbol. Make it yourself by gluing together lots of bright scraps. If cutting out the letters in cloth is beyond your abilities or too time consuming, it is sufficient to ink them in with a Magic Marker. (Note 1. Magic Markers are very IN. Have lots around. People will think you are an Underground Church artist and/or make lots of picket signs.)

9. Have something resembling a big pottery chalice on your coffee table. Don't put anything, even matchbooks, in it. IN

people, when they see it, will be convinced that you have Underground Liturgies.

10. A dove made out of any material or even painted on an old piece of wood is a good thing to have. This will let everyone know that you are in the Peace Movement. (Note 2. Underground Church artifacts should not be too well made. A rough-looking piece suggests that the maker was being Spontaneous, which is the really IN virtue.)

NOTE ON THE BATHROOM

Though not nearly as important as the living room, the bathroom is not to be overlooked. A collage pasted on the wall and made from old magazines with a few heads of the Hierarchy scattered about its surface is usually quite sufficient to demonstrate that you are with the sheep rather than the goats.

Chapter 4: How to Have Your Own Liturgy

Not so long ago the way to make it in the Underground Church was first to be invited to a Home Liturgy and then, after a novitiate of attending other people's Liturgies, one set up one's own. (Those over thirty were sometimes guiltily reminded of Anne Baxter's role in *All About Eve*.) With a scattering of episcopal permissions for Home Liturgies, the glamour and daring has somewhat gone out of the game and the result is that one wonders if it was all worth the effort and expense.

Nevertheless, for those who would like to try what is to them something new, the following suggestions will undoubtably prove inestimable.

There are two forms of Home Liturgies, (a) the Kitchen Table, Fundamentalist or Folksy, and (b) the Cocktail Table, Advanced or Sophisticated. The choice between the two depends largely on which of the two rooms, kitchen or living room, is the larger, which has more chairs and whether guests like to squat, sit on cushions or lean on a table. Elements of (a) and (b) are almost always interchanged (Spontaneity) and so no attempt has been made to separate and classify them.

ELEMENTS

1. A large pottery or glass cup. Silver is frowned upon and gold unthinkable.

2. Home-baked bread or some charming ethnic bread from a little shop around the corner or the gourmet department in one of the better stores.

3. All participants must have memorized at least one of the Beatles' songs, preferably "All You Need Is Love."

4. Any wine is acceptable but it should be in an interesting bottle.

5. A few Dylan recordings. Joan Baez will do at a pinch.

6. Some, not many, books of universal interest from which very brief readings can easily be selected, e.g., the Unpanishads, the Old Testament, the Karma Sutra.

7. The latest literary sensation should be in evidence. It gives an air of relevance to the whole proceedings but need not be read from.

8. The virtue of Spontaneity. Have and cultivate a sense of the Pneuma so as to be able to give on-the-spot virtuoso performances of Canons and relevant reflections.

Mix all the above elements and you will have a profound and, needless to say, quite existential experience, similar, so it is said, to that of the First Christians.

Chapter 5: What to Say at Cocktail Parties and Other Important Gatherings

The following should be memorized and said or chanted in a moderately loud voice. Should your memory be somewhat defective, print the text on the back of a recent copy of *The Critic* (IN). At lower-middle-class gatherings the back of "*Ave Maria*" might

do. Never be seen in public with *America*. Use a Magic Marker,
the brighter the better.

Here follows the mystic formula:

BERRIGANCORITADEWARTKUNGMcAFFEEBROWN
CALLAHANDANCALLAHANSIDNEYCOXMcKENZIE
LEONOVAKCUNNEENJUSTUSGEORGELAWLERBAUM
REUTHERBRENNANNEUHASSSTRINGFELLOW
HERRMALCOLMBOYDGROPPIBERRIGANPHIL
BERRIGANDANCORITANOVAKGARAUDYCORBIN
GABRIELMORANHAFNERSCHARPERREUTHER
HOYTTHORMANMARTINMARTYLEOMARYDALY
DEWARTKUNGCOXNOVAKBERRIGANMcKENZIE
CORITAJUSTUSGEORGELAWLERETAL

Go back to the beginning and start again.

The above incantation may be used in private devotions for
the warding off of ecclesiastical poltergeists and in the ritual puri-
fication of one's environment.

Shorter form for use when retiring:

BERRIGANKUNGCORITACOX
Save me from ecclesial pox.
                    (one quarantine under the usual conditions.)

Chapter 6: How to Bring Up Your Child

As a member of the Underground Church you will not want your
child to suffer from all the nasty, sectarian hang-ups from which
you have by now totally extricated yourself. By doing a little
reflecting on your own thrust to meaningful maturity you will no
doubt discern certain guidelines for the upbringing of your child.
However, for the sake of those of you who are more activist than
contemplative it has pleased us to set forth the following rules.
(Memorize.)

1. Soon after birth, or even prenatally, the infant should have
its budding senses stimulated by the sound of Indian temple bells
and the fragrance of joss sticks. Thus will be set a sensory founda-

tion for the appreciation, in later years, of the Great Religions of the East.

2. From the age of two the child should be exposed to the bright and appealing colors of the Time-Life books on the Great Religions. Their perusal will provide him with the beginning of a sense of religious pluralism. Bright Buddhist robes are just as attractive to a child's eye as the gold in St. Peter's Basilica.

3. One might seriously consider naming the infant after one of the founders of the non-Christian religions. This may be a truly liberating act for the parents and is not likely to make a (say) Zoroastrian out of the little American.

4. The child should be trained not to make any distinction between sense impressions derived from liberated nuns and those produced by airline stewardesses; in like manner the priest, whether in turtleneck or Roman collar should evoke no more response from the Underground child than does, for example, a policeman. All this will help the little one to think horizontally, thus avoiding the menace of hierarchical categories.

5. The practice of Home Liturgies at which there is a nice disregard for the crumbs will help the child acquire a thoroughly non-scrupulous nature.

6. Teach your progeny to regard Catholic schools as pathetic leftovers from the McCarthy era.

7. Take special care to develop his arm muscles. For exercise in this there should at all times be a picket sign proportioned to his age and physique on hand.

8. Above all, educate yourselves by learning from the child. His will be the mentality of the New Generation. By getting with it you might just avoid the Generation Gap and even be taken care of when you are old and gray and harmless.

Chapter 7: Space for Index of Names of Friends

The following blank space is provided for you to write in the names of Underground Church Friends. They will be flattered and you will doubtless enjoy adding more and more names as you follow the instructions of this Micromanual and become ever more deeply immersed in the Underground.

FINAL NOTE

You may write in names of celebrities whom perhaps you do not already know. They won't mind. Everyone in the Underground Church is so very friendly and nice.

3. *I AM A MARRIED CATHOLIC, I WANT TO BE A PRIEST!**

by Joel Wells

BECAUSE THEY HAVE never really understood me or my innermost needs, what I am about to write may be resented somewhat by my wife and five children. They may find it difficult to believe that I am not motivated by spite or selfishness, but by the deepest anguish and utterly open-hearted love. But I am through with hypocrisy and sham. The truth is that I am tired of being married, tired of being a father, and that I want desperately to become a priest.

But my desperation means nothing to society or the Church. I am caught in an age-old trap from which there is no escape. At thirty-seven I am hopelessly cut off from any hope of ever realizing my ambition. The Church will never know what it's missing—the great building drives I might have pushed over the top, the stirring homilies I might have preached, the brilliant light and wisdom I might have shed on these troubled times—all of me wasted, turned back in on myself, poured back down the drain of my own enormous potential.

My heart sinks when I think how many times single people have approached me hoping for an open and positive response

* From the September 15, 1967, issue of *Overview*.

24

to their tortured pleas to join them in a game of poker, golf, tennis, or simply a convivial after-work beer, only to be turned heartlessly aside by the only answer I can give—the only answer the system allows me to make: "Sorry, the wife's expecting me." How many times have these hands of mine which yearn to hold chalice and breviary instead been immersed in dish water or the icy depths of a clogged toilet bowl.

I could go on and on with such questions but I don't want to break your heart. Nor do I fancy that I am the only man trapped by the system. I am confident that I speak for thousands of married Catholic men whose tongues are muted by conformity and fear of "the little woman." Let me tell you the brutal truth about our lot.

Our days are spent in an endless and humiliating scramble for the dollars necessary to feed, clothe, house, educate and entertain the great brood of children we have spawned. Our evenings are consumed as a sacrifice to the insatiable maw of "close family relationships" of an intensely "I-Thou" nature such as bickering, helping with homework, taking out the garbage and paying bills.

Our much envied suburban weekends are twaddled away fixing broken windows and bikes, cutting grass, washing the rusty, rattle-ridden station wagon, and applying Band-Aids to filthy juvenile extremities while our wives rush forth on wanton shopping sprees for such luxuries as roach powder, Sani-Flush, hair spray and Lavoris (my toothpaste bill alone would keep a celibate in liquor —good liquor—for a year). While the children amuse themselves disjointing the plumbing, the repairmen come and go in sports cars paid for by the conspiratorial malfunctioning of the many ingenious appliances needed to run up my electric bill to a suitably staggering monthly total.

When my wife finally returns because her charge cards have overheated, and the children have devoured fourteen hamburgers, been hosed down and bullied off to bed, we settle down for the legendary moment known as "domestic bliss." This consists of watching the late-show on our pre-Edison model television set while indulging ourselves shamelessly with a six-pack of beer purchased in lieu of the new necktie I need. All of which is prelude to that which, for which, on account of which this whole banal life-drama is enacted—the sacred mystery of conjugal sex. Being a Catholic, of course, the unspeakable joys of this union are somewhat dimmed by the ever-present fear that my wife, whom nature has seemingly endowed with the ability to get pregnant simply by walking through a field of poppies, may conceive yet another proof and tribute to the primary end of marriage.

You will understand, then, why I yearn for the dignified, calm, and infinitely rewarding life of a priest. In addition to the spiritual stature which is automatically conferred, I yearn for those quiet evenings in the rectory, those golden hours spent in the confessional guiding and uplifting the lives of people like myself. And if, perchance, a problem or doubt should cloud the sky of priestly tranquillity, it is only necessary to turn to the wise and kindly pastor for help and warm, paternal counsel.

Not for the priest the eternal and frenetic quest for dollars; not for him the soul-shrinking breakfast full of sound, fury and flying cereal. Rather he can take comfort in the mature delights of evening walks about the parish, of stimulating conversations with his fellow priests, of a weekly round of golf, of winter vacations to Florida, of an occasional commendation from the Bishop —these are but a few of the things a priest can count on, the very things I yearn for and will never know.

There will be those, I suppose, who will mistake my anguish for envy. There will be those, too, who will say that I have oversimplified and exaggerated my case in order to make my point. It is always thus when a man dares to lay bare his soul. I can only hope and pray that the Church will heed my honest searching, and move to relax its rigid, authoritarian stance before it's too late. To insist that I—and the thousands for whom I speak —take the consequences of my vocational decision smacks of monolithic totalitarianism and cries out to heaven for redress.

If something isn't done and done quickly, I may be forced—

against all my inclinations—to bring my case before the wider forum of the American people. In the few pitiful moments I have managed to snatch for myself in the past year I have been working on a book called *A Modern Layman Looks at His Outdated Marriage*—and it's a lulu, I can tell you that.

4. *CASUALTIES OF RENEWAL**

Cartoons by Martin Murphy

"They never did figure out what went wrong."

* From the April–May 1968 issue of *The Critic.*

"*Today, a long-awaited announcement from the Vatican!*"

*"My kid says he wants to become a priest but I keep tellin' him:
'Get into something more permanent . . .'"*

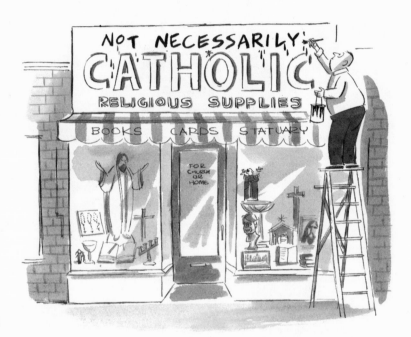

"*. . . and I ate meat on Friday, and I didn't fast during
Lent, and I went to see a 'B' movie . . . and I . . .*"

"*I don't get it! It walks, it talks, it
glows in the dark. So why don't it sell?*"

"Because those clowns at the Ecumenical Council said the Jews didn't kill Christ; that's why all of a sudden we gotta forgive the Jews for killin' Christ!"

"I'm sorry ladies, but smoking is still one of our little no-no's here."

*"Hi everybody! Welcome to another edition of the good old 9:15.
This is Ed, 5th-Sunday-after-Pentecost, Cavanaugh,
your friendly commentator, talkin' . . ."*

5. *AN AFTERNOON OF JEWISH-CHRISTIAN FRIENDSHIP**

by Margaret O'Connell

THE TWENTY-SECOND of February, a holiday common to all citizens and unimpeded by Lent, High Holidays, or Reformation Sunday, was chosen for an all-out fling at improving relations between Christians and Jews. The bewildering and disappointing "Statement on the Jews" had only been on the books a few months and, after the initial shock, hesitant steps were being taken here and there to see what, if anything, could be salvaged.

Under the joint sponsorship of the local chapter of B'nai B'rith and Immaculate Conception High School, Jewish-Christian Day had been widely publicized and invitations were sent to every Jew and Christian for miles around who had ever indicated, not interest necessarily, but merely an absence of hostility to that sort of thing.

"We can't just preach to the converted," the Archbishop, who never balked at turning an old phrase to fit a new situation, said at one of the early planning sessions, and the others at the conference table agreed. "Gotta get 'em all out," he went on. "All our people, whether they know it or not, would benefit by this . . . er . . . encounter." He looked around the table at the degrees

* From the February–March 1968 issue of *The Critic*.

of Judaism and the divisions of Christendom. "I'll have it posted on every bulletin board, in every parish. I don't know about you people," he challenged them, "but I can guarantee we'll get the Catholics out."

The others thought that was fine but declined to make any such promise themselves. They would do what they could.

The Most Reverend Francis X. Fallon had long ago but reluctantly decided to do whatever had to be done to carry out the decrees of Vatican Council II whether he agreed with them or not. And he was doing it with the same firm hand that had built his archdiocese into one of the richest in the country, with a school system unrivaled in advanced teaching methods and closed circuit television. In the matter of reform and renewal, nobody was going to accuse his bailiwick of dragging its feet.

As it turned out, the Archbishop showed up on Jewish-Christian Day only long enough to give the keynote address and shake a few choice Jewish hands. Then he went off to bless the cornerstone of a new school at the other end of his territory. But he did make good on his boast—he got the Catholics out.

Shortly after noon, cars began pulling into the circular drive in front of the high school, depositing their passengers, and going out again in search of places to park. The people waiting on the front steps for the drivers to come back were cheerful but timid, well disposed but wary, and sticking close to their own groups.

At the top of the steps an informal welcoming committee had arranged itself strategically. A burly monsignor in long cassock, purple pom-pom and sash, stood beside an absurdly small rabbi with a wrinkled yarmulka sitting on the back of his head. This was Rabbi Leonard Sackowitz, assistant at a Reform Temple in a posh suburban community. His special field of action was the anti-poverty program, but he had been sent to Jewish-Christian Day because the senior rabbi was busy correcting the proofs of his book on Christian anti-Semitism. The monsignor was the Right Reverend John A. Buckley, lately private theologian to the Archbishop at the Council, and now number one ecumenist of the

chancery office. Monsignor Buckley had a facility for turning his
hand to whatever was required of him, but his real competence
lay in the area of diocesan fund-raising. He would be happy when
things settled down again and he could get back to it.

Opposite, a middle-aged monk, whose twelfth century white
habit stopped just above his twentieth century black suede shoes,
had taken up his stand alongside a "coffee house" minister of
vaguely Methodist persuasion. Reverend Tom Bolton was rather
well known in certain unconventional circles for peace-picketing
and civil rights marching, and he had twice been arrested for
preaching, unasked, in homosexual bars. He was present only
because there was no decent way of keeping him away, and it
was hoped that putting him on the welcoming committee would
generate an identification with the "establishment," at least for
the time being.

Farther down the steps, Sister Mary Humiliata, of the Congregation of the Poor Sisters of the Sacred Names of Jesus, Mary,
and Joseph, Inc., sported a fetching "new nun" habit. Wisps of
inexperienced hair showed at the edges of a soft black veil. Sister
had no counterpart among the welcoming committee—it would
have been difficult to find one—but she managed very well on
her own, calling out hearty greetings to perfect strangers and
shaking hands with anybody who happened to come within range.

All in all it was a brave show of brotherhood, and the gather-
ing Jews and non-Jews, Christians and non-Christians responded
more or less in kind.

Inside the spacious entrance lobby, a high-ceilinged semicircle
of Vermont marble and polished oak, registration desks were
tended by groups of Immaculate Conception seniors. Each par-
ticipant was given a bright orange packet containing a number
of papers: the day's program; a mimeographed list of suggested
questions for use in the workshops; a card with the Hebrew,
Catholic, and Protestant "Grace Before Meals"; the assigned
places for lunch and workshop groups; and brochures advertising
the latest flurry of books on anti-Semitism.

Clutching their bulging packets, the Jews and Christians milled about the lobby gaping at the statues and testing each other cautiously before going into Alfred E. Smith Hall where Jewish-Christian Understanding was about to begin with a banquet lunch.

Immaculate Conception was a high-priced, high-toned school for the daughters of Catholic affluence. It had been built in the early thirties when the solitary boast of American Catholics on the national scene had been the brief, brave flame of Al Smith. His ignominious defeat at the polls bore witness to ultimate truth in the same mysterious way that his victory would have—especially after the Great Depression fell with a screaming crash around his opponent's hapless ears—and there was a sudden but short-lived rush to immortalize him in stone, bronze and verse. Over the entrance to the dining hall, a marble bas-relief of the Defeated Catholic Candidate shared the limelight with half a dozen statues of saints standing in niches along the walls.

In the center of the lobby and completely obliterating both Al and the saints from view at the front entrance, a giant-sized statue of the Virgin, eyes fixed on some celestial middle distance, reached out enormous arms indiscriminately to all the world. From the left hand, and clearly no part of the original design, dangled a small white rosary made of a waxy substance that looked suspiciously as if it might glow in the dark. This overpowering presence, which must have been intended for a mountain top, took a little getting used to. Even the Catholics gawked at it in wonder.

It was almost one o'clock when the senior girls, smiling with practiced courtesy and the brittle detachment of the very young, urged the last curious gapers to enter the dining hall and take their places. About a dozen of the interfaith elite were seated at the head table. The Archbishop, in red and gold brocade edged with lace filigree, was on the right of the rostrum, and Monsignor Buckley, his purple accessories looking almost penitential in comparison, was on the left. A conservative rabbi with a neatly trimmed beard and eyes like Jeremiah exchanged monosyllables with His Excellency, while on Monsignor's right was an Episcopal clergyman, pale and pencil thin, whose long white neck rose out of a Roman collar without touching it at any point. The places at the ends of the head table were occupied by several anonymous gentlemen who might have been Jews who didn't look Jewish, or Christians who did.

The dining hall—occupancy 300—was almost full, and the Roman collars, embroidered yarmulkas, monastic robes, plain and fancy nuns' coifs, and the inharmonious conformity of lay apparel, looked like an interpretation in human terms of "The Peaceable Kingdom," and had the same air of improbability.

Whether the Catholics were egged on by the Archbishop's thumping zeal or provoked by the Vatican Secretariat for non-Christian Religions—which was obviously not going to let the matter drop—they had pretty much the edge in numbers. Jews came in greater force than had been expected, especially by Jews. But Protestants were substantially outnumbered. Logical proportions, once it was recognized that the Catholics were providing the property and the troops and the Jews were footing the bill. This one was plainly not a Protestant show.

Lunch was a self-conscious affair served by another set of Immaculate Conception seniors. In a touching try at an ecumenical menu, the participants were offered bagels and lox, which anybody could eat if they had a taste for them, and chicken salad, which observant Jews couldn't eat whether they had a taste for it or not.

Everybody stood up with a loud clatter of chairs when the rabbi with the prophetic eyes came to the microphone to offer the Hebrew grace. And there was an uneven flutter of hands as some of the Catholics crossed themselves. The rest of the company stood with bowed heads. When they all sat down again, conversation, hesitant and polite, broke over the hall in subdued murmurs.

Rabbi Sackowitz, feeling hopelessly inadequate to the demands of the task that had been thrust upon him and terrified that his ignorance might be exposed, had been hoping for the isolation of the head table. His disappointment was acute when he found himself at one of the small tables in the midst of the Gentiles. His companions included a Presbyterian minister; a tall, gaunt sister in an extravagantly pleated, pre-Council habit; a large-faced woman with an abundance of noisy jewelry; and a middle-aged couple who bore an unnatural resemblance to each other. The couple, who were Mr. and Mrs. Fred Harris, Missouri Synod Lutherans, had light red hair, and their clothes and the color of their skin, even the "whites" of their eyes, ran together in a ruby-hued mirage. They smiled resolutely at Rabbi Sackowitz, and their Christian love, obtrusive and inexorable, seemed directed exclusively at him. He smiled back with what he hoped was a minimum of encouragement.

In his preoccupation with the rubicund Lutherans, he had not noticed that the sister was speaking to him in a broad Irish brogue, wanting to know what his "cap" was made of.

"Oh," he answered at last, blushing, "Silk, I suppose. Or . . . or cotton?" The large-faced lady also seemed interested in the material of the yarmulka, and with a quick movement he snatched it from his head and handed it to her. The two women examined it closely, fingering the cloth and peering inside at the label.

"Poplin," the sister said and made clucking sounds with her tongue.

"Rayon," said the other firmly. "I can always tell rayon."

They handed it back to him and he rolled it up and stuck it in his pocket.

At the other end of the table the Lutheran couple struggled bravely with the bagels and lox. The rest of the guests took some of both, except the rabbi, who declined the bagels in deference to new dentures and helped himself to the chicken salad, painfully aware of the disapproving eye of Jeremiah from the dais.

"Are you an Orthodox?" the large-faced lady asked, examining him with a kind of clinical concern that should have been filtered through a microscope.

"No, I'm not," he said, thanking God it was something he knew about. "An Orthodox rabbi would . . . Well, he would wear a long beard and . . ." He broke off in embarrassment, realizing that an orthodox rabbi would not even be there, let alone be eating the chicken salad, and he was promptly assailed by doubts about whether, after all, the old ways were not the best.

He was saved from extricating himself by Mrs. Harris, who launched unprovoked into a lengthy account of her kindnesses to Jews and her spectacular successes in converting souls from anti-Semitism. Her converts were wide-ranging, numerous, and bordering on pushovers. The ease with which she demolished the prejudices of cab drivers, delivery boys, strangers at bus stops, and young members of the Luther League, painted a highly implausible picture. If true, they should all be out preaching to misguided citizens instead of sitting there stuffing themselves with interfaith food. The long childish narrative was punctuated with nods and chuckles from Mr. Harris and was completely ignored by the rest of the table.

"My sister Sarah married a Jew," the large-faced lady announced before Mrs. Harris had quite finished. The remark seemed to be directed at the rabbi.

"Oh?" he said, and prayed he hadn't turned out to be a wife-beater.

"Her name is Lerner," the woman continued. "They live in Belle Haven."

"Belle Haven?" the rabbi repeated. "Isn't that interesting! Maybe he's in my congregation. . . ."

"Oh, no!" the woman said, throwing him a reproachful look. "He's not in your congregation. He's a Catholic now." She turned her microscopian eye on him again for an uncomfortable moment. "Sarah would never have married him otherwise," she said.

At the other end of the table the minister was nobly bearing the whole brunt of Mrs. Harris' continuing narrative, spoken across her husband's chest and hampered by the speaker's pathological inability to come to a full stop. Semicolons, inverted commas, dashes, exclamation points were profuse; only the period was noticeably absent. She stopped at last only when the luncheon speakers were about to begin.

After the tables had been cleared and the guests served a second round of coffee, Monsignor Buckley approached the microphone and spoke briefly in welcome. He introduced the Archbishop with the traditional flourishes, and the aging prelate rose ponderously from his seat. He placed a sheaf of papers on the rostrum, glanced once around the hall, peering out of the tops of his eyes through the tops of his bifocals, and then began to read in a stentorian voice. The gist of his message was that everybody ought to fulfill his obligation to understand and get along with everybody else, especially since the Council Fathers had recommended it. This familiar theme was given an air of freshness by a peppering of words and phrases that had come into vogue since Vatican Council II: encounter, commitment, people of God, dialog, Church in the world; and the artful dropping of the well-worn pontifical sayings: "Spiritually, we are Semites," and "I am Joseph, your brother."

When he had finished, he nodded to the wild applause and briskly left the platform. The guests buzzed briefly while the Monsignor trudged to the microphone again and introduced the next speaker, the bearded man with the piercing eyes, Rabbi Solomon Gottlieb of the American Jewish Committee.

The Rabbi gave an earnest, straightforward talk, completely devoid of humor and the kind of high comedy usually expected from Jews. After a few minutes of unanecdoted oratory, people began examining their programs and nudging each other to look at one thing or another on the day's schedule. Solomon Gottlieb, however, went bravely on and received in the end the same hearty applause as the Archbishop.

The last speaker was the thin Episcopalian, Father Jules Reed, who captured attention by speaking in a twangy Australian accent and won unreserved compassion by looking scared to death. If anything, the applause for him was slightly more enthusiastic than for his predecessors.

None of the speakers had disturbed the precarious peace by actually mentioning the recent Vatican Council "Statement on the Jews," although all three had skirted it with caution. The luncheon came to a peaceful end, with brotherhood holding firm and Jewish-Christian friendship off to a promising start. The workshops were scheduled to begin in ten minutes in the second floor classrooms, but the guests, crossing the room to greet people they knew or wished they knew, took almost ten minutes to get out of the dining hall. The Irish sister at Rabbi Sackowitz' table made off in a swirl of skirts toward a clergyman whose episcopal rank was visible only by the silver chain across his chest. The pectoral cross it held was either tucked out of sight or had been left at home. Sister tried desperately to kneel and kiss the prelate's ring but he kept her on her feet with a kind of clerical half nelson, gripping her arm with his ring hand until his eyebrows locked. It was awkward but His Excellency prevailed, and the sister, after some smiles, nods, and grimaces, submitted reluctantly and followed the crowd to the workshops.

The classrooms on the second floor were small and stuffy and smelled of chalk dust, pencil parings, and blown-out candles. They were quite large enough, however, to accommodate comfortably the 18 or 20 participants in each workshop—as far as grown people could be comfortable at desks designed for freshman high school girls. The narrow space did not bother the bird-boned Rabbi Sackowitz, who had taken a seat in the back row, but it constrained the lady two seats in front of him whose sister had married the Jewish-Christian. She shifted her position several times in a vain attempt to come to terms with the tight fit, and finally settled for bolt upright and face forward, her hands straight down at her sides. The Rabbi saw with satisfaction that she would probably not be able to turn her head more than 45 degrees to either side. With the telltale yarmulka still in his pocket, he hoped he might sit out the two hours unrecognized and undisturbed. Emboldened, he looked around at his workshop group and saw that they included, besides all his luncheon companions, Sister Humiliata of the welcoming committee, Reverend Tom Bolton of the coffee house circuit, and a number of other interesting and strangely disquieting personalities.

In front of the room, Father Reed, the thin Episcopalian, stood behind the lectern in earnest conversation with Monsignor Buckley. As moderator of the group, he was getting some last minute instructions about procedure, timing and, perhaps, a few hints about staving off outbreaks of violence. When the Monsignor departed, Father Reed stood uneasy behind the lectern waiting for Christians and Jews alike to find places and settle down.

Just inside, and out of the way of the door, a stout man with an angry expression sat in a wheelchair and scowled at the bric-a-brac of Catholic education scattered about the classroom. On the front wall over the blackboard was a large crucifix. Strips of last year's palm—dry, browning, and brittle—were stuck behind the bowed head. Two flags, the papal and the American, stood in opposite corners, and a gaudy statue of the Virgin shared a small round table with dusty paper flowers and deep blue votive lights long since gone out. The walls were adorned with mottoes and pithy sayings, mostly culled from the Lives of the Saints, and aimed at fostering humility, submission, obedience, docility, and self-sacrifice—all the virtues natural to woman when hammered in persistently from childhood on. Scrawled over the blackboards were the scattered remains of yesterday's math lesson. The man in the wheelchair squinted at them with a puzzled frown and shook his head slowly, as if the schools had clearly gone mad since he was a boy.

The workshop got off to a slow, polite start with the brotherhood of man and Fatherhood of God serving, in fact, as impedimenta to free exchange. So that it shouldn't be a total loss, the man in the wheelchair introduced the matter of the Vatican Council's "Statement on the Jews." He wanted to know (1) why they rejected the first statement and why it took so long to formulate the second; (2) why they omitted the word "deicide" from the second statement; and (3) why they saw fit to "deplore" instead of "condemn" anti-Semitism.

Most of the workshop group, including the reluctant representative of Reform Judaism, had only a vague notion of such details. The moderator, feeling unqualified to speak for the Church of Rome, waited hopefully for a volunteer. Finally, a young priest in the row along the windows stood up and began to answer. (1) They took so long because it was very important and they wanted it to be exactly right.

"But it was *not* exactly right!" exploded from the wheelchair. "They should have left it alone. It was better the way it was!"

The young priest looked hurt, but he cleared his throat and went on. (2) The word "deicide" was a contradiction, an impossibility. The Council Fathers declined to introduce it into ordinary language. The wheelchair man interrupted here to point out that the Church had been using it pretty freely for centuries, but the priest ignored him and went on to (3). "I'm not sure," he said, "why they used 'deplore' instead of 'condemn.' But it must be that 'condemn' has a specific meaning in conciliar documents. Perhaps it would imply 'binding in conscience.' . . ."

The face in the wheelchair was purple. "Binding in conscience!" the man roared. "And isn't the murder of six million Jews important enough to bind the conscience of a Christian?"

The young priest's cheeks flushed, he blinked rapidly in confusion and sat down abruptly. His expression said clearly that there was no need to shout about it, and he looked hastily around for confirmation of his position. At this point the moderator intervened and made polite remarks about its being no good crying over spilled milk. The man in the wheelchair whipped out a handkerchief and began to polish his eyeglasses furiously. He muttered something *sotto voce* about spilled milk, which made the people near him laugh. The angry color slowly receded from his face. After a moment's awkward silence, an animated discussion of the Seder ritual began. It ended with a noisy exchange of recipes among the women. Father Jules Reed, visibly relieved that a serious brush with the truth had been averted, mopped his brow with a handkerchief and sneaked a quick look at his watch.

Another discordant note—more of a recurring motif—occasionally threatened the peace and purposelessness of the two hours. A spare little woman, middle-aged and highly nervous, tried repeatedly to start discussion on one of the questions on the list of suggestions. The question, neatly loaded, read: "Do you believe there is any truth to the myth of the intellectual superiority of Jews?" The nervous lady was vociferous in her stand that Jews were, indeed, intellectually superior to the rest of mankind—and no myth about it!

"Just examine the evidence," she urged her unwilling listeners. "Who are all the lawyers and the doctors and the professors? Who are all the artists and the scientists?"

It was difficult to tell whether she was Jewish herself or if this was some newer and subtler form of anti-Jewishness. Her excited tone conveyed nothing but her excitement. The moderator, perhaps to satisfy his own curiosity, asked her to identify herself.

"I'm Mary Mulcahy," she said crossly, preferring to stick to the subject, "from Prompt Succor."

"From what?" the Australian twang emerged in a squeak and Father Reed cleared his throat and said again, "From what, please, Madame?"

"Prompt Succor," Mary Mulcahy repeated. "That's my parish. Our Lady of Prompt Succor."

Father Reed nodded slowly, not at all sure she wasn't putting him on. A silence descended and the little woman, recognizing that the moment had somehow slipped by, sat down to wait for the next opportunity. In spite of several earnest tries, however, she was unable to draw anybody into discussing the intellectual superiority of Jews. The Christians were loathe to examine it even as a myth, and the Jews were embarrassed by it and felt they had enough trouble already.

Impressed by the strange little woman's exalted opinion of Jewish intelligence, Rabbi Sackowitz hoped fervently that she would never happen upon one of his Bar Mitzvah classes. It would be fatal to her illusions, and his persecuted people, like Charlie Brown, needed all the friends they could get.

Near the end of the workshop session, one of the nuns, a quiet one with an unusual habit of navy blue wool and a stiffly pleated coif that prevented her from seeing right or left, took the floor and began to describe her recent visit to the Holy Land. The account of her progress from holy place to holy place, in which Franciscans from Washington, D.C., kept popping up to read appropriate Scriptures, was delivered in a fluttery falsetto and there was heavy concentration on the places of the New Testament. She told of visiting the spots where Jesus, whom she consistently referred to as "Our Lord," was born and where he died, where he changed the water into wine, multiplied the loaves and fishes, and cured the woman afflicted with an issue of blood. As the documentary wound on, her voice began to falter and it seemed to her anxious audience that if she continued much longer she would surely break down. But she finally appeared to stop, overcome, at the site of the Transfiguration, where three temples had been built; one to Moses, one to Elias, and one to "Our Lord."

But just as Father Reed was getting ready to speak, she recovered herself and began again. This time her voice was harsh with urgency. She looked around the room, turning her head to see beyond the pleated coif, and beseeched her listeners with raised eyebrows and outstretched hands.

"How can you people not accept Our Lord?" she cried suddenly, and shocked everybody into an embarrassed silence. "I don't understand you," she said, raising her voice. "How can you people live among all these holy places and not believe in Our Lord?"

The moderator looked around in alarm and his neck stretched another inch out of his collar like the stem of an outraged tulip. Several people stirred uneasily and looked at each other out of the corner of their eyes. The man in the wheelchair was the first to find his voice. He had been sitting slumped in his chair for the past half hour in an attitude of sulking unconcern. Now and then he shook his head slowly with a melancholy air. When he spoke, it was without anger, almost without interest.

"What people do you mean, Madame?" he asked, turning slightly to look at the nun. She had remained standing, waiting for a quick answer to her two-thousand-year-old question. "Nobody here lives in the Holy Land." She did not answer at once and he went on in a tone of exaggerated patience. "And what about the Arabs? Most of the places you mention are in Jordan. How can the Arabs live among the holy places and not believe in your Lord?"

"But . . . ," the sister stammered. "Our Lord was a Jew! One of your own people! I should think you'd . . . you'd. . . ." She broke off in confusion and looked pleadingly at the man in the wheelchair, who had slumped down again and turned his back on the group. He had clearly retired from the discussion, and the sister did not go on.

Another man, not heard from before, rose majestically in the middle aisle. Portly and serious, a blue-black shadow accumulating on his heavy jowls, he addressed his remarks carefully to the moderator.

"I don't think," he began importantly, "this is quite what we are here for. It seems to me that we ought to be discussing facts —especially things we have in common."

"Like what?" someone asked from the back of the room.

"Like belief in one God," the man answered, still addressing the moderator.

Mrs. Harris, the Lutheran, suddenly jumped to her feet and shouted in a voice so strident with venom that it startled Rabbi Sackowitz out of a private reverie he was enjoying.

"Aha!" she said, pointing her finger at the man in the middle aisle. "But that's the whole thing right there! The whole thing! We believe in *three* gods!"

In the stunned silence that followed, the rabbi began to suspect that he had been day-dreaming and had missed something very important. He could not otherwise account for the sudden violence of gentle Mrs. Harris, the convert-maker. But when, in the next moment as if on cue, the room roared with laughter, he joined in the outburst from sheer relief.

Father Reed banged on the lectern with the palms of his hands. "Here now! Here now!" he shouted above the noise, asserting his imaginary authority. The laughter did not stop on command but surged up for an instant and only then snickered to a stop.

Father Reed stared at the reddish lady, who had gone considerably redder, and stammered into the last of the stifled chuckles, "Are you a . . . a . . . . I mean . . . . What *are* you, Madame?"

"I am a Missouri Synod Lutheran," Mrs. Harris replied stanchly, in a tone that proclaimed she was quite ready to burn at the stake for it.

"But surely," the moderator implored. "Surely, Madame, you believe in the Trinity! Three Gods in one . . . . I MEAN," he fairly shouted, correcting himself. "I mean three persons in one God."

"Well, of course," the lady acknowledged impatiently. She pointed her finger at the man again. "He knows what I mean. I mean we believe in Christ Jesus and he doesn't!"

Unaccountably, the workshop participants thought this exceedingly funny and broke once more into wild laughter. Some of the ladies took out tissues and dabbed at their eyes. The men, the more portly ones, hugged their sides. But the serious gentleman in the middle aisle did not think it was funny at all. He turned to face Mrs. Harris, threatening immediate explosion. Not waiting for the laughter to die down, he shouted across the room.

"What the devil do you mean?" he demanded furiously. "I am a born Catholic! I am a Grand Knight of the Knights of Columbus! I'll have you know . . ." He blustered and could not continue. Instead he reached up and grabbed the lapel of his jacket, thrusting the K. of C. emblem forward with his thumb like some indisputable badge of authenticity. His darkening lower jaw jutted out behind it.

Like laughter in church, there was no stopping it now, and the room rocked uncontrollably again as the guests began to see that ecumenism could be fun.

Mrs. Harris opened her mouth and gasped. She retreated at

once, leaning toward her husband, who sat in the seat ahead and
did not seem to understand the meaning of the laughter. "I thought
he was a Jew," she whispered, and giggled behind her hand.

The man in the wheelchair, his sublime detachment and dis-
interest gone all out of control, shook convulsively and perspira-
tion gathered on his brow. He made agonizing little whining
sounds, as if the whole experience was hurting him, physically,
and gasped for breath. When Monsignor Buckley suddenly opened
the door and stared in alarm at the rollicking workshop, he was
almost knocked over as the wheelchair scooted past him and
raced down the hall to the elevators. Its occupant, still laughing
and probably lost forever to the cause of Jewish-Christian friendship, disappeared for the rest of the day, and the wind-up session
in Alfred E. Smith Hall had to go on without him.

The hall had been cleared of the luncheon tables, and rows of
wooden chairs were set up, turning the dining room into an audi-
torium. On the stage where the head table had been was a lectern
trailing microphone wires, and behind it another row of wooden
chairs. The moderators, who were about to report on the results
of their workshops, made their way to the platform, and the rest
of the crowd found places among the benches in the hall.

Rabbi Leonard Sackowitz, exhausted by the frenzy of the afternoon, and bewildered by the whole proceedings, slid into a seat
in the rear of the hall and watched the others come in. About
half the original company had remained and they all took seats
toward the rear, leaving the first four rows empty. Everybody
seemed tired and anxious to go home.

Monsignor Buckley went up to the platform with plodding steps
and stood at the lectern shuffling papers and waiting for the hall
to settle itself. When it was almost quiet, he began in a tired
voice to introduce the moderators, who were five in number. As
they gave their reports, Rabbi Sackowitz stared at the neck hairs
of the man in front of him and calculated the possibilities of
getting to Belle Haven before dark. Apparently, the other four
workshops were no better. Hassles about why the Jews refused

to accept Christ alternated with accusations of Christian persecu-
tion over the centuries. Unfortunately it was not possible to convey
the wild hilarity that had broken out in his own workshop or he
might have tried. It seemed a desperately needed contrast, even
a glimmer of hope.

Saddened by so much hostility, especially among people whose
very presence proclaimed their good intentions, the rabbi tuned
out the reports and fell to wondering if Jewish-Christian dialog
would not result in more harm than good. He was tempted once
more by the serenity of the old ways, the proud isolation of
Orthodox Judaism, forever immune to such futile and unpleasant
adventures. And once more he rejected it. Catholics, he mused,
must also be tempted to return to a militant and uncompromising
past; and Protestants to the rigid zeal of the early reformers. The
old ways hadn't done much, he conceded finally with a sigh, and
new ways had to be tried. Still, the afternoon had wearied him
and before the last report was given, he slipped quietly out of
the hall.

In the darkening, deserted lobby he fumbled for his coat and
then stood still, listening to the high, clear, sing-song of the nuns,
far off, chanting their evening office in post-Conciliar vernacular:

> *For the Lord has chosen Si—o—on*
> *He prefers her for his dwelli—ing . . .*
> *Sion is my resting place forev—e—er*
> *In her will I dwell for I prefer h—e—er . . .*

Stepping briskly around the skirts of the giant Virgin, he paused
at the front entrance and turned to look up at the impassive stone
face. "You don't look Jewish," he said aloud. Smiling to himself,
he pulled the yarmulka out of his pocket, slapped it on the back
of his head with a flourish, and went out. The faraway voices of
the nuns followed him down the steps.

> *The Lord bless thee out of Si—o—on*
> *Mayest thou see the good things of Jeru—usal—e—em*
> *All the days of thy l—i—i—fe . . .*

6. *HOW TO PASS FOR NEW BREED**

by Hubert Horan, W. F.

THE INTELLIGENT OLDER PRIEST'S GUIDE
TO THE NEW BREED CLERGY AND RELIGIOUS,
OR, A HALF-BREED'S FIELD MANUAL ON
ACCOMMODATION TECHNIQUES

THE FIRST POINT to be remarked is that no one will *say* of himself or herself that he or she is "New Breed." You are supposed to know without having been told. This is the first barrier. Further, the term itself is somewhat like the older "egghead": it is vaguely insulting to be called one directly, but it is directly and sharply insulting to be told that one is not, or has not the qualities of, the "New Breed."

The second general point is that it is essential not to let oneself be thrown off the track, or "snowed." It may appear to be an impossible task to speak the new language or act the new way; it is not. A few simple passwords and conventions will suffice to pass muster on ordinary occasions, just as a few expressions and mannerisms and tags sufficed to help one pass muster in older times. Radical reform of oneself is no more necessary

* From the December–January 1968 issue of *The Critic*.

now than it ever was; if it were, there would be no new breed. Mass movements can never afford to make too many demands on their adherents in practice, however demanding the public exhortations of their leaders may appear to be.

The general guidelines which follow apply, unless otherwise specifically stated, to both the male and the female of the species —or breed.

1. Social Occasions

The new breeder likes to regard himself as a brother to all men. Hence you will be wise to avoid using titles of any sort, either religious or civil. A good ploy is to avoid even last names: don't give yours, and don't use theirs. If possible, use an outrageously "folksy" nickname, both in introducing yourself and in greeting others. If dealing with lay people who feel uneasy about calling a priest simply by his first name, use "Padre" instead of "Father." You should, of course, avoid like the plague of your choice calling other priests "Father" or Sisters "Sister."

It helps to be able to play a musical instrument, or at least be able to sing protest songs. If you have the misfortune to be tone deaf, the best thing to do is to learn a variety of parody songs and to sing them as off-key as possible.

Artful casualness is another keynote. It helps to have the complete assortment of Peanuts sweatshirts. Let it be known that one or another is reserved for special occasions—say, the Snoopy one with "Surf's up" on it. You can then use this as a gentle and thoughtful way of honoring people on their birthday. Sisters, in particular, are very sensitive to this sort of thoughtful gesture. These sweatshirts also make tasteful and much-appreciated ordination or religious profession gifts.

While on the subject of gift-giving, there is one point to be noted particularly with reference to Sisters. In the old days, it required limitless subtlety to give a Sister a present. One would call at the convent with a book of spiritual reading, with a tasteful card and a carefully impersonal dedication on the flyleaf. The book would be received by the Superior or her delegate, and a huge bookplate would be placed over your words on the flyleaf, and the book would be placed in the convent library without a word to the Sister of your choice.

Nowadays the way is to be a *nuance* less subtle. First of all, you should elect something along the lines of a white elephant. Last year's six-by-four-foot inflatable Easter egg, white with foulard designs in fluorescent Day-Glo colors, used in supermarket displays, would be an example. These can be had quite cheaply through the managers of supermarkets, can be carried deflated in an attaché case to the convent, and inflated at the nearest gas station. Use lighter-than-air gas for an extra touch. It is preferable to make delivery at night, both to avoid being seen with a six-by-four phosphorescent egg in tow and to add to the needed touch of being a bit much. Ring the convent bell, ask to speak to Sister So-and-So, and, as you hear her coming, hide behind the egg, float it gently in toward her, and say in your best imitation Peter Lorre voice, "Eet is bigg-air zan boz of us." Results are guaranteed every time, and you can at least be sure that your gift will not be buried somewhere in the library.

A ploy much appreciated is that of calling casually on any new breeder and saying that the mailman has not delivered your copy of *NCR* that week and could you please borrow his. Alternatively, you could ask his advice about new readings in theology, mentioning in passing that you are very disappointed in Rahner, Schillebeeckx, et al., in that they don't go far enough. A priest who asks anyone else's advice about theology will immediately step out of the "old fogey" classification, even if he does not immediately make it as an honorary new breeder born out of time.

You can also display a dartboard, with a picture of some prominent Church conservative as the bull's-eye, in your room or office. Humorous signs, Peanuts calendars, wall posters, the milder sort of goodies from your corner psyche-delicatessen, bumper stickers and buttons of the right sort will all make the right sort of initial impression. Someone coming in will think that you are "open to dialogue," i.e., one of them. Avoid overdoing it, of course, or they may smell a trap.

While it is definitely not cricket to strike first, it may well happen that you will have to strike back in self-defense at some enemy who is slandering you. There are several ways of doing this which will permanently make him as the heathen and the publican to any self-respecting new breeder (n.b.-er).

If the enemy is a priest, spread rumors that the bishop is going to make him a monsignor; that will be the end of his influence, and he will be avoided by new breeders like germs avoid a friend who has caught penicillin in Roger Price's old Droodle. Less drastically, whether priest or not, you can plant a copy of *The Mind of Pius XII* on his desk behind his back. He will have great difficulty explaining *that* away.

You could also say that he gives sermons on the Mystical Body, say, or that you saw a stub in his checkbook for a contribution to save *Triumph*, or that he has a signed picture of Cardinal Ottaviani under the framed picture of Bonhoeffer on his desk, or that he still meditates—with a book. The idea is to pick out one or another damaging assertion which is almost impossible to disprove.

It should, perhaps, be mentioned in passing that it is not wise to agree out of hand with a new breeder. The idea is to answer with a pained, "Well, of course," if he or she makes a particularly far-out assertion or criticism and occasionally to say that, while you respect his opinion very greatly, yet there is room for disagreement among men of goodwill. Most of the clichés of nineteenth-century secular liberalism are currently in honor among twentieth-century religious liberals—but not all. Be sure of your ground before plagiarizing from Rousseau, for instance; this would often be a bit too advanced still. (Rousseau, of course, is eighteenth century, but in n.b. parlance anything before 1955 is nineteenth century. One of the characteristics of the n.b. is ignorance, and therefore syncopation, of the Western tradition.)

A few special points should be mentioned with regard to Sisters. It is sometimes wise to address them on first meeting, in spite of the general ban on titles of any sort, as "Miss" and then to proceed immediately to say that her new habit is *so* aggiornamentoed that she could be taken for a lay woman. To back up the initial good impression this will make, you can then offer her a Tiparillo. If the hour and the circumstances permit you to offer her a drink, ask her what sort of cocktail she would like. If she names one of the commoner sort, ask her if she would like it dry, or with vodka instead of gin, etc.—look impressed. If she orders something a bit unusual, look impressed again and ask her what it is. But be careful here; it is possible that you are not the only one of the two who is putting on an act to impress the other, and you may even embarrass her.

If you are both a bit more civilized and prefer wine, ask her advice about wines and years before ordering. It is a wise gesture, if at a banquet or restaurant, to tell the *sommelier* beforehand to compliment the Sister on her choice.

If the Sister you are meeting is the Superior, it is tactful to tell her that you never would have guessed it. It is very bad indeed these days to look like a Superior, and such encouragement from an outsider will be long remembered.

2. Totems and Taboos

Like any sub-culture struggling along in times of change, the new breed of professional Christians has its rallying banners and its ritual likes and dislikes and avoidance patterns. These are relatively simple to learn, but a misstep can be very costly indeed. The important thing to note is that these totems and taboos are ritualistic and therefore compulsive, not rational. Do not, therefore, feel uneasy about conforming; regard them merely as the rules of a social game. Do not take these heroes or villains too seriously yourself, of course. It is merely a case of when in Rome, eat spaghetti.

The totems vary a bit from year to year. There is not too much of a visible pattern. Still, you will not go far wrong in quoting Bonhoeffer, in any context. If you do have an original thought or two, attribute them to him or say that they are a development of his thought, and you will find ready audience. Among American n.b.-ers, who are still a bit backwards, Teilhard de Chardin is still popular. Conclude any sermon or talk with, "As Teilhard says, '*L'histoire humaine n'est que le soulevement progressif de la nappe humaine,*' " and don't translate. They will be terribly impressed; whereas to say, "Human history is just the progressive lifting up of the human tablecloth," is definitely less impressive, and some may even suspect that you are burlesquing their hero. Be vague. It's safer.

Pop culture, such as *The Sound of Music* or Peanuts, has ritual importance in some respects; but be careful that you choose the right elements of pop culture.

Words like "community," "inner city," "dialogue," etc., are always useful in casting a spell; the key word is, of course, "love," which can as always be used pretty much as one wants, like the blank tiles in Scrabble. One should, of course, be very careful never to say "charity" instead of love, or "Holy Ghost" instead of Holy Spirit; this would be an all but irremediable *faux pas*. Use also "committed" and "commitment" wherever possible—but be careful to avoid the basic verb form "commit" or the other noun "commission," which are definitely not n.b. Eclecticism in semantics as well as ideology is characteristic of the n.b. For them, the world and the Church are not a solidary whole, but a sort of cosmic smorgasbord from which they pick and choose according to a more or less arbitrary pattern. It is best not to try to fathom the pattern; that would lead you into very shallow waters indeed. Protective imitation is here, as generally in any unfamiliar territory, the safest guide.

Taboos, or ritual avoidance patterns, are equally important. Just as the legendary Irish heroes had their *geasa,* so do the new breed. Just as Cu Chulainn was brought to his ruin by not following the *geasa* of his strength—like the *geis* of not eating dog's flesh and that of not passing any cooking fire without eating—so you will come to grief and even unforgivable downfall if you violate the taboos of the n.b. tribe.

It should not be necessary to point out that one should never mention St. Thomas or use Latin under any pretext. Popes previous to John XXIII and after Pope St. Clement I are equally not to be referred to, except, of course, unfavorably. President Johnson's name, even, is best not mentioned at all. No prelate or military man above the rank of corporal, specialist 3c, or petty officer 3c should ever be referred to, even with overtones of understanding or approval.

Singly, these taboos are not too difficult; it is the collective weight of them which can sometimes cause trouble. Like Scylla and Charybdis, one is always ready to snatch up those who avoid the other. I know of a very clever French Benedictine who was obliged, for very serious reasons, to allude to some scholastic theologians in the course of a talk against Canon Law. He thought that the tone of his talk, which was quite radical, would justify a passing allusion to thirteenth-century thinkers, provided he made that allusion critically and obviously under duress. So intent was he on avoiding this pitfall that he fell into another: he used a Latin phrase. He said, "We might even be obliged to consider positions taken by (*horresco referens*) scholastic theology." Wanting to avoid the Scylla of seeming to accept scholasticism, he was sucked into the Charybdis of using a bit of Latin, and that was the last anyone ever heard of him outside of his monastery. Be warned!

3. Liturgical and Other More Formal Occasions

Anyone who seriously reads any reasonably open Catholic periodical will have no difficulty in recognizing what is demanded of him by the new breed in this line. Floating parishes, pop vestments, new compositions, and apparently bold statements which can all be explained away later on are all parts of the picture. With a bit of imagination, it will not be hard to conform to the n.b. pattern sufficiently to get by. No special pointers will be needed here on general principles.

Some particular points, however, might be helpful for those who wish to go further. The intelligent older priest will, of course, be very careful indeed never to be caught celebrating Mass by himself: Concelebration will give him a chance to gain points in out-breeding (or in-breeding, depending how you look at it) the n.b. One good way is the path of studied casualness in vesting. If you wear an alb, don't wear a stole; if a stole, don't put on an alb. Do not go too far, however. If you are wearing only slacks and your Peanuts sweatshirt, wear a stole and possibly also an amice, or a stole of a color which shows up clearly against the background of your sweatshirt, so that you will be visibly one of the celebrants. Otherwise, someone from Nerdsville who might have wandered in by mistake might be shocked and cause trouble with the Establishment prematurely.

Another excellent way really to make your presence as a real senior n.b.-er will sometimes present itself. It may happen that there are not enough copies, or no copies, of the English Canon of the Mass available. This is often the case on the first day or days of clergy meetings. Watch the principal celebrant; if he is not alive to all that is new and good, he may decide to start the Canon in Latin, figuring that there will always be enough old missals around in Latin so that the other celebrants can take part. Let him get well into the *Te Igitur*, then pull out one or several copies of the Canon in some unknown tongue, any unknown tongue. The Canon in KiSwahili, for instance, can be ordered here from the TMP Bookshop, P.O. Box 399, Tabora, Tanzania, East Africa, at about thirty cents a copy. You whip the offending Latin text away, and with a penetrating whisper of "We can use the vernacular these days, buddy!" you substitute the KiSwahili text on the missal stand. You will also gain a reputation for being very mission-minded and knowledgeable if you distribute copies to the others and say, "Just pronounce the consonants like in English and the vowels like in Italian [do *not* say 'Latin'] and accent on the second last syllable." This will establish you forever, in the minds of all present, as a true vernacularist. Should anyone be enough of an old breeder (o.b.-er) to point out that more of those present can understand Latin than KiSwahili, stare at him and say, "Vatican II says that the whole People of God is essentially missionary." This will get you lined up for talks in schools and convents on missionary theology, as well as liturgical theology.

In case you are the only celebrant before a group of n.b.-ers somewhere, the idea is (a) not to let yourself be surprised or astonished by anything they do, and (b) if possible, to do something which will surprise or astonish them.

On point (a), the essential is to keep a poker face and try to think fast enough to come up quickly with a comeback. If, for instance, at a convent school, suddenly at the offertory there comes a procession of nuns and students dancing gracefully down the aisles with baskets of bread and bottles of wine balanced on their heads, and playing electric guitars and singing over transistor microphones with an amplifier speaker under the altar when you are just reaching for the chalice, don't let your hand tremble or your pupils dilate. Go them one better. If you can vault gracefully over the altar and go with a delicate *entrechat* to meet the offertory procession and then successfully juggle the whole lot— i.e., just the loaves and bottles and guitars, not the nuns and students—while returning to resume where interrupted, you will uncontestably have gained the day, as dramatically and decisively as ever good King Harry at Agincourt, in spite of heavy odds your attackers thought were in their favor.

I have thought it necessary to specify that it is not necessary to attempt to juggle the students and nuns as well; beginners always tend to overdo it a bit and to complicate things too much for themselves. The simple and tasteful touch always succeeds better. The golden mean of the classics is still a valid principle.

Should you, however, wish to express it, better say *mēden agan* rather than *ne quid nimis*. Greek can still be used, as it is a living language; Latin not.

Point (b), that of surprising and astonishing the congregation, is best left to the abilities of each would-be senior n.b.-er. The action or word has to be personal and individual, and what works for one priest will often not be at all appropriate for another. One might have very good results in inhaling helium during a sermon on the Ascension, in order to dramatize the old notion of physical rising. Another might not make it off the ground at all with this idea, or at least not until after serious dieting.

These few pointers will suffice to indicate some of the broad lines of approach to the sort of mini-ecumenism required of us in dealing with the rising generation of clergy and religious. Using these guidelines as a basis, the intelligent older priest should come gradually to acquire a series of reflexes which will permit him to gain all the necessary arts of survival. Ten thousand may fall by his right side, but not he who follows the way outlined above.

7. *CARTOONS BY KIERAN QUINN**

Underground Church

* From the October–November 1968, December–January 1968, February–March 1969 issues of *The Critic*.

"Now what's all this about a credibility gap?"

Birth control IS *wrong*

"Pssst . . . . . Charles Davis is right"

"*Will you be my 'Encounter in Christ'?*"

8. SIX VERSIONS OF A PRAYER YOU'VE HEARD SOMEWHERE*

Six Versions of a Prayer you've heard Somewhere

by Joel Wells

As eavesdropped
in the field
by our far-flung
correspondents

HIPPIE OR MALCOLM BOYD VERSION

Hey Dad!
You're really out there,
Your name's a blast.
Make our scene as cool as yours.
Spread
A little bread around our pads,
But don't zap us, like,
We don't burn straights when they bug us.
From work in all its forms,
Please steer us clear.
And keep Ronald Reagan off our backs.
How 'bout it, man?

TRADITIONALIST VERSION

Right Reverend God,
Who resides in that big chancery in the sky,
Live up to your Old Testament reputation
And get things back in order here below.
Give baptized, practicing Catholics
Their rights and privileges,
And forgive us for Vatican II,
Just as we will try to forgive
Those sneaky Jews.
Lead us not into experimental liturgies
But deliver us from the Dutch Catechism.
Amen.

Art by Marilyn Fitschen

* From the October–November 1967 issue of *The Critic*.

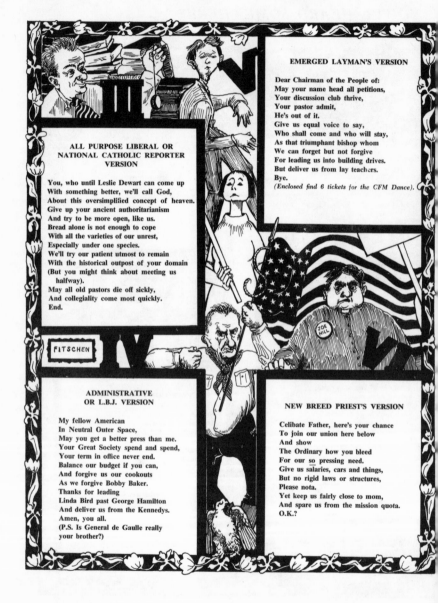

EMERGED LAYMAN'S VERSION

Dear Chairman of the People of:
May your name head all petitions,
Your discussion club thrive,
Your pastor admit,
He's out of it.
Give us equal voice to say,
Who shall come and who will stay,
As that triumphant bishop whom
We can forget but not forgive
For leading us into building drives.
But deliver us from lay teachers.
Bye.
(Enclosed find 6 tickets for the CFM Dance).

**ALL PURPOSE LIBERAL OR
NATIONAL CATHOLIC REPORTER
VERSION**

You, who until Leslie Dewart can come up
With something better, we'll call God,
About this oversimplified concept of heaven.
Give up your ancient authoritarianism
And try to be more open, like us.
Bread alone is not enough to cope
With all the varieties of our unrest,
Especially under one species.
We'll try our patient utmost to remain
With the historical outpost of your domain
(But you might think about meeting us
    halfway).
May all old pastors die off sickly,
And collegiality come most quickly.
End.

FITSCHEN

**ADMINISTRATIVE
OR L.B.J. VERSION**

My fellow American
In Neutral Outer Space,
May you get a better press than me.
Your Great Society spend and spend,
Your term in office never end.
Balance our budget if you can,
And forgive us our cookouts
As we forgive Bobby Baker.
Thanks for leading
Linda Bird past George Hamilton
And deliver us from the Kennedys.
Amen, you all.
(P.S. Is General de Gaulle really
your brother?)

NEW BREED PRIEST'S VERSION

Celibate Father, here's your chance
To join our union here below
And show
The Ordinary how you bleed
For our so pressing need.
Give us salaries, cars and things,
But no rigid laws or structures,
Please nota.
Yet keep us fairly close to mom,
And spare us from the mission quota.
O.K.?

9. *ONE FOGGY DAY**

by David Lodge

It was Adam Appleby's misfortune that at the moment of awakening from sleep his consciousness was immediately flooded with everything he least wanted to think about. Other men, he gathered, met each new dawn with a refreshed mind and heart, full of optimism and resolution; or else they moved sluggishly through the first hour of the day in a state of blessed numbness, incapable of any thought at all, pleasant or unpleasant. But, crouched like harpies round his bed, unpleasant thoughts waited to pounce the moment Adam's eyelids flickered apart. At that moment he was forced, like a drowning man, to review his entire life instantaneously, divided between regrets for the past and fears for the future.

Thus it was that as he opened his eyes one November morning, and focused them blearily on the sick rose, three down and six across, on the wallpaper opposite his bed, Adam was simultaneously reminded that he was twenty-five years of age, and would soon be twenty-six, that he was a post-graduate student preparing

* From *The British Museum Is Falling Down*, by David Lodge. Copyright © 1965 by David Lodge. Reprinted by permission of Holt, Rinehart and Winston, Inc., and MacGibbon & Kee, Ltd.

a thesis which he was unlikely to complete in this the third and
final year of his scholarship, that the latter was hugely overdrawn,
that he was married with three very young children, that one of
them had manifested an alarming rash the previous evening, that
his name was ridiculous, that his leg hurt, that his decrepit scooter
had failed to start the previous morning and would no doubt fail
to start this morning, that he had just missed a first-class degree
because of a bad Middle English paper, that his leg hurt, that
at his primary school he had proved so proficient in the game of
who-can-pee-highest-up-the-wall of the boys' outside lavatory that
he had wetted the biretta of the parish priest who happened to be
visiting the playground on the other side of the wall at the time,
that he had forgotten to reserve any books at the British Museum
for this morning's reading, that his leg hurt, that his wife's period
was three days overdue, and that his leg hurt.

But wait a minute. . . . One of these mental events was unfamiliar. He could not recall any sensation of pain in his leg on
retiring the previous night. And it was not, he reflected bitterly,
as if he had enjoyed any strenuous physical activity *after* retiring. When Barbara's period was overdue, neither of them
felt much inclination for sex. The thought of another pregnancy
had a dampening effect on desire, even though they knew the
issue must be already settled, one way or another, in Barbara's
womb. At the thought of that womb plumping with another life,
a spasm of cold terror coursed through Adam's bowels. In a year's
time he should, with luck, have completed his Ph.D. and obtained
some kind of job. It was essential that they should avoid conceiv-
ing another child at least until then. And if possible for ever.

How different it must be, he thought, the life of an ordinary,
non-Catholic parent, free to decide—actually to *decide*, in calm
confidence—whether to have or not to have a child. How different
from his own married state, which Adam symbolized as a small,
over-populated, low-lying island ringed by a crumbling dike which
he and his wife struggled hopelessly to repair as they kept anxious
watch on the surging sea of fertility that surrounded them. It was

not that, having produced three children, he and Barbara would now, given the opportunity, actually will them back into non-existence; but this acceptance of new life was not infinitely elastic. Its extension had limits, and Adam thought they had now been reached, at least for the foreseeable future.

His mind turned, as it not infrequently did, to the circumstances which had brought them to this pass. Their marriage more than four years ago had been a hurried affair, precipitated by the announcement that Adam, who was doing his National Service after graduation, was to be posted to Singapore. Shortly afterwards he had proved to be suffering from an ear condition which had restricted him to home postings. This had been a source of joy to them at the time, but in gloomy moments Adam wondered retrospectively whether it had been altogether fortunate. In spite of, or perhaps because of being widely separated—he in Yorkshire and Barbara with her parents in Birmingham—and coming together only on weekend leaves, they had managed to produce two children during his army service.

They had embarked on marriage with vague notions about the Safe Period and a hopeful trust in Providence that Adam now found difficult to credit. Clare had been born nine months after the wedding. Barbara had then consulted a Catholic doctor who gave her a simple mathematical formula for calculating the Safe Period—so simple that Dominic was born one year after Clare. Shortly afterwards Adam was released from the Army, and returned to London to do research. Someone gave Barbara a booklet explaining how she could determine the time of her ovulation by recording her temperature each morning, and they followed this procedure until Barbara became pregnant again.

After Edward's birth they had simply abstained from intercourse for six months of mounting neurosis. Having managed, with some difficulty, to enter the married state as virgins after three years' courtship, they found it hard that they should have to revert to this condition while sharing the same bed. A few months ago they had applied for help to a Catholic marriage counselling organization, whose doctors had poured a kindly scorn on their amateurish attempts to operate the basal temperature method. They had been given sheets of graph paper and little pieces of cardboard with transparent windows of cellophane to place over the graphs, and recommended, for maximum security, to keep to the post-ovulatory period.

For three anxious months they had survived. Unfortunately, Barbara's ovulation seemed to occur late in her monthly cycle, and their sexual relations were forced into a curious pattern: three weeks of patient graph-plotting, followed by a few nights of frantic love-making, which rapidly petered out in exhaustion and renewed suspense. This behavior was known as Rhythm and was in accordance with the Natural Law.

From the next room came a muffled thump and a sharp cry, which modulated into a low whining that Adam attributed hesitantly to his youngest child, Edward. He glanced sideways at his wife. She lay on her stomach, sucking a thermometer. A small peak in the bed-clothes further down indicated the presence of a second thermometer. Unable to decide on the relative accuracy of the oral and rectal methods of taking her temperature, Barbara had decided to employ both. Which would be all right as long as she could be relied upon not to confuse the two readings. Which Adam doubted.

Catching his eye, Barbara muttered something rendered unrecognizable as a human utterance by the presence of the thermometer, but which Adam interpreted as, "Make a cup of tea." An interesting example of the function of predictability in casual speech, he mentally observed, as he pulled back the bedclothes. The linoleum greeted his feet with an icy chill, and he pranced awkwardly round the room on tiptoe, looking for his slippers. It was difficult, he found, to limp and walk on tiptoe at the same time. He discovered his slippers at last in his shirt-drawer, a minute plastic doll made in Hong Kong nestling in the toe of each. He hurriedly donned his dressing-gown. There was a distinct nip in the air: winter was contending with autumn. It made him think of electricity bills. So, when he looked out of the window, did Battersea Power Station, looming vaguely through the morning fog.

After filling and switching on the electric kettle in the kitchen, Adam made his way to the bathroom. But his eldest child had forestalled him.

"I'm passing a motion," Clare announced.

"Who else is voting?" he cracked uneasily. In theory, Adam fully supported his wife's determination to teach the children an adult vocabulary for their physical functions. But it still disconcerted him—perhaps because it was not a vocabulary he had ever used himself, even as an adult. And it seemed to him positively dangerous to encourage the articulacy of a child so precociously fascinated by physiology as Clare. When Barbara had been in labor with Edward, and a kindly neighbor had hinted archly, "I think you're going to have a baby brother or sister," Clare had replied: "I think so too—the contractions are coming every two minutes." Such feats were the source of a certain pride in Adam, but he couldn't help thinking that Clare was missing something of the magic and mystery of childhood.

"What's voting?" asked his daughter.

"Will you be long?" he countered.

"I don't know. You just can't tell with these things."

"Well, don't be long, please. Daddy wants to use the lavatory."

"Why don't you use Dominic's pot?"

"Daddies don't use pots."

"Why don't they?"

At a loss for an answer, Adam retreated to the kitchen. Where he had gone wrong, of course, was in categorically denying that daddies used pots. Daddies often used pots. Eighty per cent of the rural dwellings in Ireland had no sanitation of any kind, for example. The correct gambit would have been: "*I* don't use pots." Or, better still: "*You* don't use pots any more, do you, Clare?"

The kettle began to boil. Adam suddenly wondered whether he had overestimated the function of predictability in casual speech.

Supposing Barbara had not said, "Make a cup of tea," but "Edward has fallen out of his cot," or "My rectal thermometer is stuck?" He hastened back to the bedroom, pausing only to peep into the children's room to assure himself of Edward's safety. He was quite all right—placidly eating strips of wallpaper which Dominic was tearing off the wall. Adam made Edward spit them out and holding the moist pulp in his outstretched hand, proceeded to the bedroom.

"You *did* want me to make a cup of tea?" he inquired, putting his head round the door.

Barbara took the thermometer from her mouth and squinted at it. "Yes," she said, and replaced the thermometer.

Adam returned to the kitchen, disposed of the pulp and made the tea. While waiting for it to draw he mentally composed a short article, "*Catholicism, Roman*," for a Martian encyclopedia compiled after life on earth had been destroyed by atomic warfare.

ROMAN CATHOLICISM was, according to archaeological evidence, distributed fairly widely over the planet Earth in the twentieth century. As far as the Western Hemisphere is concerned, it appears to have been characterized by a complex system of sexual taboos and rituals. Intercourse between married partners was restricted to certain limited periods determined by the calendar and the body-temperature of the female. Martian archaeologists have learned to identify the domiciles of Roman Catholics by the presence of large numbers of complicated graphs, calendars, small booklets full of figures, and quantities of broken thermometers, evidence of the great importance attached to this code. Some scholars have argued that it was merely a method of limiting the number of offspring; but as it has been conclusively proved that the Roman Catholics produced more children on average than any other section of the community, this seems untenable. Other doctrines of the Roman Catholics included a belief in a Divine Redeemer and in a life after death.

Adam put the tray on the floor outside the bathroom, and entered purposefully. "Come on, you're finished," he said, lifting Clare from the seat.

"Wipe my bottom, please."

He obliged, washing his hands afterwards to set a good example. Then he guided Clare firmly to the door.

"Can I stay and watch?"

"No. There's a biscuit for you on the kitchen table, and one each for Dominic and Edward."

Adam micturated, and considered whether to wash his hands a second time. He decided against it. On re-entering the bedroom, he found Dominic urging his mother to rise.

"Up, up!" screamed the child, and pulled off the bedclothes, exposing Barbara with her pajama trousers pulled down to her knees and a thermometer protruding from her rump. Barbara was the callipygian type, and Adam felt duly grateful to Dominic.

"You look like a glass porcupine with all those things sticking out of you," he remarked, to give himself an excuse for lingering on the view.

Barbara yanked at the bedclothes and plucked the thermometer from her mouth. "Don't be rude. Do you think I enjoy this performance every morning?"

"Well, yes, I do, as a matter of fact. It's like our friend Camel and his pipe. You were both weaned too early. But this latest development . . . It strikes me as a bit kinky."

"If you don't shut up, I'll break these damn things over my knee and——"

"Have a cup of tea," said Adam conciliatingly.

"Just a minute." Barbara entered the readings of her two thermometers in a small Catholic diary. This was not a conscious irony on her part, but Adam followed the relationship between the liturgical year and his wife's temperature chart with interest. He practiced a special devotion to those saints whose feast-days fell within the putative Safe Period, and experienced disquiet when a virgin martyr was so distinguished.

"Up, up!" shouted Dominic, red with anger.

"Dominic," said Adam, "Clare has got a bikky for you."

The child trotted out. They sipped their tea.

"I wish you wouldn't use those silly baby-words, Adam."

"Sorry. I keep forgetting. What was your temperature?" At this stage of Barbara's cycle, her temperature was of largely academic interest, except that marked changes from day to day might indicate that conception had taken place. Another cold wave of fear rippled through Adam's frame at the thought.

"One said 97.8 and the other 98.2."

"What does that mean?"

"It's down a bit. . . . I don't know."

"Have you . . . You haven't started your period yet?" he asked wistfully.

"No. I don't think so."

"Go and find out," he wheedled.

"Give me a minute."

How lovely it would be if she came back from the bathroom and said yes. How happy his day would be. How transfigured the British Museum would appear. With what zest he would collect his books and set to work. . . . But he had forgotten to reserve any books. That meant a long delay this morning. . . .

"Eh?" he said, conscious that Barbara had asked him a question.

"You haven't listened to a word I've been saying."

"Yes I have," he lied.

"What did I ask you, then?"

He groped around in his mind for a likely question. "You said, why was I limping?"

"There, you see? I said, 'Have you looked at Edward's rash?'"

"I didn't exactly look. But I don't remember noticing it."

"I hope it isn't measles. Why *are* you limping anyway?"

"I don't know. I think I must have pulled a muscle."

"What?"

"In the night."

"Don't be ridiculous. How could you pull a muscle when you were asleep?"

"That's what I don't understand. Perhaps I run in my sleep."

"Perhaps you do other things in your sleep," said Barbara, getting out of bed and leaving the room.

Her words did not immediately sink into Adam's consciousness. He was fascinated by a mental picture of himself running through the streets of London in his pajamas, at tremendous speed, chest out, arms pumping, mouth swallowing air, eyes glazed in sleep.

PAJAMA ATHLETE SMASHES RECORD

Early yesterday morning late-night revellers were astonished by the sight of a young man clad in pajamas speeding through the streets of London. Herman Hopple, the British Olympic coach, spotted the mystery runner when returning to his Bloomsbury hotel, and having a stopwatch in his pocket, timed him at 1 minute 28.5 seconds as he lapped the British Museum before disappearing in the direction of Battersea. An official of the A.A.A. who was fortunately accompanying Mr. Hopple at the time later measured the perimeter of the British Museum at exactly 800 meters. The pajama athlete has thus smashed the world record, and qualifies for the $10,000 prize established by an American millionaire for the first man to cover the distance in less than a minute and a half. "We are very anxious to trace him," said Mr. Hopple this morning.

Barbara's words suddenly formed up and came resoundingly to attention in his mind. *Perhaps you do other things in your sleep.* Could you, he wondered, and not remember it? That would be the supreme irony: to conceive another child and not even be conscious enough to enjoy it. There was that night not long ago when they had come back from Camel's place drowsy and amorous from drinking Spanish wine. . . .

Barbara returned from the bathroom and shook her head at Adam's hopeful glance. She was carrying Edward under her arm, breech presentation.

"I've been thinking," said Adam, "about what you said just now. It's just possible you know. That evening we came back from Camel's. Do you remember, the next morning my pajama trousers were on the floor and two buttons had come off your nightdress?"

"Don't be ridiculous," said Barbara, rummaging in a drawer for a nappy. "*You* might not know what you were doing, but I would."

"It's not ridiculous. What about *incubi* and *succubae*?"

"What about them?"

"They were demons who used to have intercourse with humans while they were asleep."

"That's all I need," said Barbara.

"How many days overdue are you?" Adam asked. As if he didn't know.

"Three."

"Have you been that much before?"

"Yes."

Barbara was bent over the wriggling torso of Edward, and her replies were muffled by the safety pins in her mouth. Barbara always seemed to have something in her mouth.

"Often?"

"No."

"How often?"

"Oh, for God's sake, Adam!"

Barbara clicked the second pin shut, and let Edward slide to the floor. She looked up, and Adam saw with dismay that she was crying.

"What's the matter?" he wailed.

"I feel sick."

Adam felt as if two giant hands had grasped his stomach and intestines, drenched them in cold water, and wrung them out like a dishcloth. "Oh Jesus," he murmured, employing the blasphemy he reserved for special occasions.

Barbara stared hopelessly at Edward, crawling across the linoleum. "I can't think how we could have made a mistake. My temperature went up at the right time and everything."

"Oh, Jesus," Adam repeated, aloud. When his own innate pessimism was balanced by Barbara's common sense, he could survive; but when Barbara herself was rattled, as she clearly was this morning, nothing could save him from falling deeper into despair. He would see it was going to be a bad day, of a kind he knew well. He would sit slumped at his desk in the British Museum, a heap of neglected books before him, while his mind reeled with menstrual cycles and temperature charts and financial calculations that never came right. He made a brief mental prayer: "Please God, let her not be pregnant." He added: "And I'm sorry I swore."

"Don't look at me like that," said Barbara.

"Like what?"

"As if it was all my fault."

"Of course it isn't your fault," said Adam testily. "Or mine either. But you don't expect to see the Lineaments of Gratified Desire all over my face, do you?"

The entrance of Clare and Dominic put an end to further conversation.

"Dominic says he's hungry," Clare announced, accusingly.

"Why aren't you having any breakfast, Mummy?" asked Clare.

"Mummy doesn't feel well," said Adam.

"Why don't you feel well, Mummy?"

"I don't know, Clare. I just feel sick."

" 'ick," said Dominic sociably.

"*I* only feel sick *after* I eat things," observed Clare. "So does Dominic, don't you Dominic?"

" 'ick."

"Sick, Dominic. Say 'Sick.' "

" 'ick."

"I wish to hell you wouldn't talk so much at breakfast, Clare," Adam said.

"Don't lose your temper with the children, Adam." Barbara intervened. "Clare is only trying to teach Dominic."

Adam swallowed the last morsel of his bacon without relish, and reached mechanically for the marmalade. Barbara intercepted him, "Actually," she said, "I feel better now. I think I'll have some breakfast after all."

Songbirds! A ray of sunshine! Bells ringing! Adam's heart lifted. Barbara smiled faintly at him and he raised his newspaper before his face to hide his absurd joy. An advertiser's announcement caught his eye:

> Write the second line of a rhyming couplet beginning:
> *I always choose a Brownlong chair*
>
> . . . .
> —and win a new three-piece suite or £100 cash.

Now that was the kind of competition a literary man ought to be able to win. A modest prize, too, which should cut down the number of competitors to a reasonable size. *I always choose a Brownlong chair.* . . . Because . . . because. . . . Ah! He had it. He read out the terms of the competition to his family.

" '*I always choose a Brownlong chair*.' What about the next line?"

"Because it's made for wear and tear," suggested Clare.

"That's what I was going to say," said Adam, resentfully.

When Adam came to dress, he could not find a pair of clean underpants. Barbara came into the room at this point, carrying Edward.

"I don't think he's got measles after all," she said.

"Good. I can't find a pair of clean pants."

"No, I washed them all yesterday. They're still damp."

"Well, I'll just have to wear the pair I had on yesterday." He moved towards the soiled linen basket.

"I washed those, too. While you were having your bath last night."

Adam came to a halt, and rounded slowly on his wife.

"What are you telling me? D'you mean I haven't got a single pair of underpants to wear?"

"If you changed them more often, this wouldn't happen."

"That may be so, but I'm not going to argue about personal hygiene at this point. What I want to know is: what am I going to wear under my trousers today?"

"Do you *have* to wear something? Can't you do without for once?"

"Of course I can't 'do without'!"

"I don't know why you're making such a fuss. I've gone without pants before." She looked meaningfully at Adam, who softened at the memory of a certain day by the sea.

"That was different. You know the trousers of my suit are itchy," he complained in a quieter tone. "You don't know what it's like, sitting in the Museum all day."

"Wear your other trousers, then."

"I've got to wear the suit today. There's a post-graduate sherry party."

"You didn't tell me."

"Don't change the subject."

Barbara was silent for a minute. "You could wear a pair of mine," she offered.

"To hell with that! What d'you take me for—a—transvestite? Where are those damp ones?"

"In the kitchen somewhere. They'll take a long time to dry."

In the passage he nearly tripped over Clare, who was squatting on the floor, dressing a doll.

"What's a transvestite, Daddy?" she inquired.

"Ask your mother," Adam snarled.

In the kitchen, Dominic was tearing the morning paper into narrow strips. Adam snatched it away from him, and the child began to scream. Cravenly, Adam returned the newspaper. He looked at the clock and began to get angry at the way time was slipping away. Time when he should be at work, work, work. Plowing ahead with a thesis that would rock the scholarly world and start a revolution in literary criticism.

He found a pair of underpants in a tangle of sodden washing in the baby's bath. Improvising brilliantly, he pulled out the grill-pan of the electric stove, wiped the grid clean of grease with a handkerchief, and spread out his pants. He slotted home the grill-pan, and turned the switch to High. Fascinated, Dominic stopped tearing up the newspaper and watched the rising steam. Adam stealthily confiscated the remaining portion of the newspaper. The competition again caught his eye.

> *I always choose a Brownlong chair*
> *Whenever I relax au pair.*

No, it was worth going in for seriously.

> *I always choose a Brownlong chair*
> *For handsome looks and a price that's fair.*

Didn't scan very well.

"Dadda, 'ire," said Dominic, tugging gently at his sleeve. Adam smelled burning cloth, and lunged at the grill. Ire was the word. He stuffed the scorched remains of his underpants into the garbage pail, burning his fingers in the process.

"More, Dadda," said Dominic.

In the passage Adam met Barbara. "Where did you say your pants were?" he asked casually.

"In the top left hand drawer." She sniffed. "You've burned something."

"Nothing much," he said, and hurried on to the bedroom.

Adam, who hitherto valued women's underwear on its transparency, now found himself applying quite different standards, and deploring the frivolity of his wife's tastes. Eventually he located a pair of panties that were opaque, and a chaste white in hue. Unfortunately they were also trimmed with lace, but that couldn't be helped. As he drew them on, the hairs on his legs crackled with static electricity. The clinging but featherlight touch of the nylon round his haunches was a strange new sensation. He stood thoughtfully before the mirror for a moment, awed by a sudden insight into sexual deviation.

"Mummy says a transvestite is a poor man who likes wearing ladies clothes because he's silly in the head," remarked Clare from the door.

Adam grabbed his trousers and pulled them on. "Clare, how

many times have I told you not to come into this room without knocking. You're quite old enough to remember."

"I didn't come in. I'm standing outside," she replied, pointing to her feet.

"Don't answer back," he said dispiritedly. What a mess he was making of his parental role this morning. Oh, it was going to be a bad day, all right.

Adam's family lined up in alphabetical order to be kissed goodbye: Barbara, Clare, Dominic and Edward (seated). When the principle behind this nomenclature dawned on their friends they were likely to ask humorously whether Adam and Barbara intended working through the whole alphabet, a joke that seemed less and less funny to Adam and Barbara as time went on. Adam kissed Barbara last, and scrutinized her for signs of pregnancy: coarse-grained skin, lifeless hair, swelling breasts. He even looked at her waistline. With an immense effort of rationality, he re-minded himself that she was only three days overdue.

"How do you feel?"

"Oh, all right. We must try and be sensible."

"I don't know what we'll do if you're pr——"

"*Pas devant les enfants.*"

"Eh?"

"That means, not in front of us," Clare explained to Dominic.

"Oh, yes," said Adam, catching on. "I'll phone you later."

"Try and do it when Mrs. Green is out."

Dominic began to snivel. "Where Dadda going?" he demanded.

"He's going to work, like he always does," said Barbara.

"At the British Museum," Adam said impressively. As he closed the door of the flat, he heard Clare asking Barbara if there were any other transvestites at the British Museum.

10. *I WAS WRONG**

by Archbishop Paul J. Hallinan

CERTAINLY, readers of *The Critic* cannot take seriously the idea that a bishop could in all honesty admit, "I was wrong."

Bishop are right. In matters of faith we make no mistakes. In public issues our opinions are sacrosanct. In finance, building, art and literature we have no peers.

This correctness of bishops, serious though we take it, seems to make little impression on bankers, intellectuals and many of the laity in general. Priests have been known to question it. Sisters, the wiser sex, usually ignore it. We suffer accordingly.

A case in point concerned the election in 1958 of the jolly peasant whom we vaguely recall as the roly-poly pontiff between Pius and Paul. I was a brand-new bishop that year, and His Holiness and I got off to a bad start because he was elected right in the middle of my own Ceremony of Consecration. Headlines were switched. "RONCALLI ELECTED POPE" was spread-eagled across eight columns. "HALLINAN A BISHOP" was relegated to page 4 somewhere between "Dear Abby" and the Dow-Jones averages. Somehow, John XXIII took the first round.

Shortly after his election, I was asked by the press to comment

* From the April–May 1968 issue of *The Critic*.

on the new pope. I marvel now at the accuracy of my observations. History will surely be reluctant to alter any detail.

I said knowingly that John would be an "interim pope." I may have used the word "caretaker." After all, he was seventy-seven. I pointed out that the words and deeds of Pius XI and XII needed time to be absorbed. Surely we can expect no encyclicals such as theirs. In fact, we could hardly expect a man of John's age to do anything spectacular. He would bless the crowds from his windows after saying the *Angelus* for them. Occasionally, some trusty would write a nice, safe encyclical—on indulgences or the dangers of secularism—and sign the Pope's name.

The reporter asked, "Because of his informality, could we expect some changes in the liturgy?" (He had been reading *Worship*!)

"Hardly," I beamed. "The rubrics have been fixed for centuries, and what was good enough for the Council of Trent fathers is good enough for us. And besides, any tinkering with the Mass might cause us to lose our inestimable treasury of the Latin language. Just think, no matter where we travel. . . ."

He was fidgeting as though he had been through this before. He changed the subject. "And other churches—will there be any efforts toward unity with other Christians?"

"You mean Protestants, of course," I corrected him firmly. "We have always been open to receive them if they come on our terms."

The reporter grew a little nasty. "Sort of an unconditional surrender? No quarter to Luther and Wesley? Are they not our brothers?"

"But they are separated," I protested.

"All right then, separated brethren."

My reply was devastating, "The term is ridiculous." (It was at this point I noticed a *Commonweal* sticking out of his coat pocket.)

The interviewer being a journalist could hardly be expected to appreciate my theological bombs. He returned to the Pope. "Do you think John XXIII will try to change the Church's attitude toward the world?"

"Come, come, let's be realistic." I tried not to be dogmatic. "The world is full of secularism, materialism, communism, dirty movies, conniving politicians and evil. The Church is full of— well, bishops and other saints, the Holy See, the sacraments, consecrated virgins and pious, devoted laymen. Between the two, there is not exactly a wall, but surely there is little in common."

I summed it all up. "No, Pope John is a good simple man. He will do little that history will note. He will keep the barque of Peter high on a mountain top while the tillers sow the seed."

He looked puzzled. Journalism majors usually do. "Would you go over that last part again? Are the tillers tilling the boat or the soil?"

I was caught, but I escaped. "That's a papal play on words."

"I see," he concluded glumly.

Nearly ten years have passed, but nothing has happened to change my early opinion of our beloved interim pope. Vatican II came and went. *Mother and Teacher* and *Peace on Earth* came and went. The rapprochement with communism came and went. Protestants attended the Council. English replaced the liturgical Latin. Hardly a thing changed. I was right.

I have recently been asked to assess the next Presidential race. It's Harold Stassen all the way!

11. *A QUESTION OF DEGREE**

by Charles Healy

MONSIGNOR CAREY, dozing in a red, imitation-leather chair in his room, jumped awake so sharply that his breviary slipped from his lap to the floor. Rubbing his eyes, he looked slowly about the room as if he had not fully expected to see it again; past seventy and of uneven health, he knew that even a cat nap could easily stretch into eternity. Thus he never went to sleep without his breviary or beads at hand, determined, as it were, to die with his boots on. He hoped, in fact, that by so arranging himself (as if God were susceptible to the power of suggestion), he would insure that he would die quietly and painlessly in his sleep.

Monsignor sincerely mourned the death of any of his friends, but he could not help taking some secret consolation in their passing. Though his faith was unshakeable, he did not feel any overwhelming confidence in eternity, for he simply could not imagine millions upon millions of centuries of endless variety, painless and beautiful. There were occasions, in fact, when, if the choice were put to him, he would have chosen oblivion over heaven, although in his heart he knew that it would be as

* From the October–November 1964 issue of *The Critic*.

promised, and he would be grateful. In the meantime, he would console himself with the fact that so many of his friends had preceded him and would cushion his own fall into paradise.

Monsignor squinted at the clock on the dresser. It was well outside the clear-cut circle of his vision, so he reached into the inside pocket of his cassock for the glasses which, their stems folded under like the legs of a yoga, were sitting on the dresser in front of the clock.

As he brought his hand out of his cassock, Monsignor noticed in the palm a smudge of red. He held his hand close to his face and squinted at it, amazed. Could it be? After a moment he held up the other hand. It too, it seemed, was bloody. Monsignor dropped his hands, palms up, to his lap. He was as exhausted by the discovery as if he had done some strenuous exercise.

It was significant of Monsignor's personality that he accepted the fact of the stigmata so quickly. He was a practical man, an administrator, always had been. He began his ministry in the chancery and had remained there—through three bishops—until he had been given this parish, a choice plum. As a pastor, he remained as distant and mysterious as he had been in his former position, moving quietly through the corridors on such small steps, the skirt of his cassock exhaling behind him, that he seemed to be on wheels. He was like a celebrity in his own parish: everyone knew who he was, but he knew practically no one. The two curates served as his subtitles: "The Monsignor says you can use the church hall for the meeting Thursday night," Father Fonda would say, standing in the rear of the church between Monsignor and one of the parishioners. Only a desire not to embarrass the curate kept the parishioner from acidly replying, "Will you tell the Monsignor I said thanks?"

Only once, shortly after he had come to St. John's, did Monsignor attempt to break the mold and become, to some extent, a "people's priest." Seeking a safe area of contact with his new flock, he had decided on their children. He knew that the smallest smile aimed at a child was enough to satisfy the parents that its author was a person of warmth and discernment, and they would not ask for more. Indeed, Monsignor had often seen a whole roomful of intelligent company rendered speechless, or, at the very least, incoherent, by the insertion of a child into its center.

So, Monsignor took to kissing babies. His bent, bussing figure at the rear of the church on Sunday mornings became as familiar as the holy water font. But the practice ended as suddenly as it had begun.

One Sunday morning, Mrs. Robert Allen, the mother of five, arrived for Mass with her small brood. The first four children filed past Monsignor, each receiving a kiss. Mrs. Allen, who had been making last minute adjustments in all the children's outfits right up to the door of the church, brought up the rear with Marjorie, her youngest. Intent on tying Marjorie's pinafore and being in a position similar to Monsignor's, she turned absentmindedly when she came opposite him and planted a quick kiss on his cheek.

Though there were only three witnesses to the incident and though their discretion was unimpeachable, Monsignor was never again seen in the rear of the church in any but an upright position. An experienced spiritual tracker, he read the kiss as sign that higher powers disapproved.

So Monsignor, the practical priest, accepted the stigmata in his own peculiarly philosophical way. He did not worry about the fact that no wounds crouched in hideous beauty under the blood, for he vaguely remembered from his Lives of the Saints that they sometimes appeared gradually in the beginning, coming and going at certain intervals, usually every Friday. He wondered about his worthiness, but decided that no one was really worthy to wear the stigmata, and so it became a question of the degree of unworthiness, whether he was less unworthy than another. Of course, there was the possibility that the choice was not made entirely for spiritual reasons. For example, from a physical or geographical viewpoint, Monsignor was the obvious choice. His parish was centrally located with plenty of hotels and restaurants to accom-

modate the thousands of pilgrims who would inevitably and endlessly come. On Sundays, he was sure they would be given the
use of the municipal parking lot which ordinarily stood all but
empty on that day. Now, if Father Coleman, for example, had
been selected to bear the stigmata, the situation would have been
quite different. His parish was on the east side of town where
the streets were narrow and twisting and, at certain hours of the
day, gagged with grocery carts. There were no hotels to speak
of and most of the restaurants were of the greasy spoon variety.
Monsignor Carey concluded that, if the choice had been up to
him, he would have had to choose himself.

Relieved, he pushed himself out of the chair and started for
the bathroom. He kicked his breviary, and it shot across the room
ahead of him, scattering holy cards. He picked them up, replaced
them in the breviary, placed the breviary on the bookcase, then
stepped into the bathroom.

It was not until the last of the red liquid had swirled out of
sight that he realized he was washing a first-class relic down the
drain. Well, there would be plenty more where that came from,
he thought grimly.

Monsignor returned to the bedroom, and, hearing voices
outside, moved to the window. As he watched his two curates
walking over from the church where they had been hearing
confessions, it occurred to Monsignor that he would soon be
hearing confessions again, for people were known to travel incredible distances, often on foot and in all sorts of weather, to
receive spiritual advice from a stigmatist. His shoulders drooped.
He frankly hated hearing confessions and had not, in fact, heard
any since he had become a pastor—unless you were to count the
few times he had happened on an accident or made an ill-timed
visit to the hospital. (Sometimes, walking into the hospital rooms
of parishioners who had been reported "doing nicely" and finding them clinging to life with a much fainter grip than the one
they quickly fixed on his arm, he wondered if someone was
pulling his leg.) He realized that it would not look good if,

after the stigmata had become permanent and public, word got around that he hadn't heard confessions in years. Not that he was remiss. As pastor, it was his privilege to hear confessions or not. But at the same time, it was his duty, where possible, to avoid scandal, even unjust scandal. Perhaps that was why the wounds were not yet permanent: to give him time to get back into harness. It was something to think about. A short time later, thinking about it, he went down to dinner.

Monsignor stood at the head of the table, the plates stacked in front of him. The tip of the carving knife appeared, disappeared and reappeared at the side of the roast like a silver serpent's tongue. One by one the slices of red meat slumped and piled on the platter. Monsignor placed several slices on each dish, added a portion of potatoes and vegetables and passed one to each of his curates.

When they had finished their dinner, Monsignor rang the bell to summon the cook. The bell was a mate to the one used at Mass, and Father Dennis, the younger of the two curates, could not hear it rung without hearing an invisible congregation sliding wearily to its knees. Conversely, when the bell was rung during his Mass, he saw, instead of the host or chalice which he held elevated over his head, Monsignor sitting at the dinner table absently twisting one of the red buttons of his cassock as if it were a control knob with which he was trying to tune in Rome.

Esther slammed into the dining room without ceremony, employing the same heavy tread which formerly was responsible for the spasmodic jumping of the television picture in the priests' study. They had uncovered this fact one night by carrying out a plan of Monsignor's. Monsignor sat in the study in front of the television, Father Fonda was stationed on the second floor at the head of the stairs and Father Dennis stood nervously outside Esther's room at the rear of the house. When he heard her leap out of the chair and start across the room to exchange a *Look* for a *Life* from a library of such literature on her bureau, he signaled to Father Fonda, who called to Monsignor, who reported to them when they returned to the study that the television had indeed gone haywire at precisely that time. Monsignor, who was the first to point the finger of suspicion at Esther, was so pleased that they had solved the problem—the repair man had been summoned three times and had finally laid the blame on fallout—he called for sherry all around. They were on their second glass when it occurred to Father Dennis, who had been feeling giddy right after the first glass, that the incident was not unlike the gospel in which a rich man returns home from seeing Christ and finds that the fever left his dying son at the very moment the man himself was speaking to Christ. He was about to share this intuition with the others when the television began to act up again, and they realized that they had uncovered the cause of their trouble but not the cure. This last was eventually accomplished by presenting Esther with a new radio, a phonograph and a television set (with, of course, remote control). Although these did not have the intended effect of keeping Esther in her seat, they did so clutter her tiny room that a trip to the bureau now required a series of sharp turns and detours which precluded any of her long, heavy steps.

Rather than walk around the table, Esther leaned over as far as she could, then tossed Father Dennis' jello dish the last few inches so that the dish spun around like a coin before coming to rest. For Esther, this was a minor offense. When she was in a hurry to get out in the evening (to where, God could only guess), she would carry their plates away before they were finished and, if they lingered over dessert and coffee, she would turn the dining-room lights on and off like a nun signaling the end of a high school dance. On the other hand, when she had time to kill, she would hover about the table rearranging serving dishes suggestively and urging them to "clean up" everything. "Wanna finish these?" she would ask, holding the potato dish over one of their plates, the serving spoon cocked. If anyone hesitated— plop!—the potatoes landed on his plate and Esther wheeled and marched triumphant to the kitchen, her great buttocks alternately punching at her dress like two doomed cats.

For something which fought so desperately to get off the spoon, the jello was remarkably docile once inside the mouth, allowing itself to be strained repeatedly through the teeth until it was restored to its original liquid state and swallowed. This process was occupying the attention of the two curates when Monsignor announced, "I'll take confessions tonight."

Both priests were understandably alarmed; Monsignor's delinquency in the matter of hearing confessions was a favorite topic of conversation. They had, in fact, been discussing it earlier when they noticed that he was watching them from his bedroom window. Now, looking at each other in surprise, they wondered if he could have heard them, although, given the distance and Monsignor's imperfect hearing, this seemed impossible. On the other hand, it now appeared that nothing was impossible.

"What?" said Father Fonda, needing time to think.

"I said I'll take confessions," Monsignor snapped back. "You two can decide whose box I'll take."

"Whose box?" Father Fonda repeated, needing more time.

"Well, I don't have any place to go," said Father Dennis.

"Neither do I," said Father Fonda quickly.

"Then stay home!" Monsignor said. "What's the problem?" With that he pushed his chair back and left the room. The two priests looked at each other, shrugged, and went after him.

They found him in the study watching the television warm up, and took chairs on either side of him. At one time there had been a comfortable couch in the study, but one Saturday night Monsignor and Father Fonda were watching television with a visiting Jesuit when Father Fonda fell asleep and slumped over so that he was resting against Monsignor. Monsignor was barely able to budge him, and when he looked to the Jesuit for help he realized from the way he was frowning at the television that he was obviously trying not to look, as if he thought the curate went to sleep every night with his head on Monsignor's shoulder. A few days later the couch was replaced by two straight-backed chairs which the curates now occupied.

"They'll probably be pretty heavy tonight," Father Fonda said without looking away from the television.

"That's right," said Father Dennis. "That rain around four kept a lot away."

"Yeah, I got all my office said."

A little later Father Dennis offered, "Gee, that box is hot."

"And that seat is like a board."

Monsignor, feeling himself weakening, stood up, placed his collar around his neck, tucked in the goatee-like rabat, snapped the collar button and fled.

A little later, he stepped into the confessional with all the enthusiasm of someone putting on wet trousers. Before pulling the door to, he checked his equipment: the switch for the red light outside which indicated that there were no penitents inside (he hoped he would have occasion to use it); the arm-rests just below the screens on either side of him; the small ledges near the floor on which he could break the monotony for his feet. He took out his rosary beads, slowly unknotted them and let them dangle from his fingers. Then, unable to think of anything else to do, he leaned forward and closed the door, sealing himself in.

From the steady flow of penitents, Monsignor judged that Father Fonda, whose confessional he was seated in, was either a good confessor or an easy one. He decided he was the latter, because, as a rule, people didn't care for a "good" confessor; the admonitions and advice he offered kept them in the confessional too long and they knew what those succeeding them in line would think: the same things they themselves thought when someone stayed in the confessional for more than a few minutes.

Monsignor realized that, if judged by this one stint, he too would be considered an easy confessor. He was too busy with his own thoughts (whenever his hands perspired, he held them in the thin strip of light which came in between the door and examined them just to be sure; he also worked his feet around to see if there was any pain or if his socks were wet and sticking to his feet) to say more than, "For your penance say three Our Fathers three Hail Marys make a Good Act of Contrition."

Around quarter to nine, when he was thinking of slipping out early, the sound of bones cracking told him that someone was in the confessional shifting from knee to knee to attract his attention. He shut off the light and pushed the slide back. Immediately a boy of about ten started rattling off his sins.

"Bless me father for I have sinned. This is three weeks since my last confession I accuse myself of. Talked during Mass three times, looked at magazines I shouldn't once . . ."

As the boy droned on down his list of sins, real and otherwise (at one point he admitted "crossing against the light" and Monsignor made a mental note to have another talk with the nuns), Monsignor became aware of something—a breathing other than the penitent's. He squinted through the screen, but it was too dark.

"Who's there?" he asked.

The boy stopped speaking, but there was no answer.

"I said, who's there?"

"It's me, Father," answered a voice near his shoulder.

"Monsignor," corrected Monsignor.

"It's me, Monsignor."

"Who else?"

"Who else?"

"Who's with you? I know there's two of you."

There was a long pause.

"Well . . . ?" Monsignor finally said.

"He's my friend, Father."

"Monsignor!"

"Monsignor."

"What's he doing here?"

"He's just listening."

"Listening! What do you mean listening?"

"He's not a Catholic like us."

Monsignor wisely abandoned questioning the penitent. That "us" told him the boy was prepared to come over to his side against his non-Catholic friend.

"What are you doing here?" Monsignor asked. There was no

answer at first, then there was a muffled sound as if one had punched the other.

"Nothin.' " The second voice was behind and above the other and Monsignor felt an unreasonable anger that the boy was not even kneeling.

"Nothing!"

"I don' know. I just wanted to see what it was like. *He* said I could . . . ." Another punch, only harder.

"What's the matter with you?" Monsignor asked the lower darkness. "You can't bring people in here. Get out, both of you!"

"Yes, Father . . . *Monsignor!"* There were scuffling sounds as the two fought to get out, then a quick glimpse of light as the curtain was displaced and fell back.

As soon as they had gone, Monsignor remembered that he should have gotten their names—the Catholic boy's at least. In his anger, he had taken "It's me" as positive identification. He knew it was too late to catch them, but the sexton or someone might have seen them. Pulling himself to his feet, he opened the door and came face to face with Mrs. Whiteley.

Nora Whiteley, even at eighty-six, lived in constant fear that her voice would be recognized in the confessional. She was old enough and slowed enough to have the priest come to her home, but she had no intention of making it that easy for him. Instead, she made her way to church where she filtered her sins through a handkerchief and kept her head down because you could never be sure that priests, what with all those years of sitting in the dark, listening, hadn't developed a special sight. In Nora Whiteley's case, some of her fears were well founded: there was a distinctive crack in her voice which no number of handkerchiefs could disguise. This crack also identified her as the would-be anonymous voice which called the rectory periodically to keep the priests on the straight and narrow. She once called to tell Father Fonda that he was a wild, carefree man, unfit to wear the collar, and that he was sure to burn in hell for certain offenses which were never clearly defined. When he pressed to know who was calling, she said, "A friend," and hung up.

On another occasion, when she called to warn Father Dennis against sins of the flesh, he remembered that earlier that day, when he was driving several cheerleaders to the CYO basketball game, he had driven past Mrs. Whiteley's house. She must have seen him from the upstairs window where, taking advantage of the lace curtains which gave her a clear view of the street while making her invisible from outside, she kept an almost constant watch. Occasionally, Mrs. Whiteley did strike bone. This time, however, she had come quite wide of the mark.

When he was twelve years old, young Michael Dennis had had an unsolicited look up his aunt's dress as she fell heavily into a chair. He saw there, besides the flesh rising like bread above the stockings, such a complex of nylon, elastic and silk, that he thought, for her, dressing must have been like packing a parachute. (Did that long strap, when pulled, release all her undergarments so that they fell in folds at her feet?) It is just possible that at that moment, subconsciously, the future Father Dennis decided never to marry.

"Did you see them?" Monsignor asked Mrs. Whiteley, whose bright eyes glared at him over her handkerchief.

"What's that?"

"There were two of them," Monsignor said, turning hopelessly back to the confessional. He knew that she could not have seen them, for she would have been walking with her head down, searching the near darkness with eyes and stick. She stood leaning on her cane like a golfer waiting for her partner to take his shot, staring after him.

Monsignor allowed her enough time to get into the confessional, then opened the slide. He saw her silhouetted at the entrance holding the curtain aside. For a long moment they stared at each other. Finally, Mrs. Whiteley hissed, "Peeping Tom!," dropped the curtain and moved away.

Back at the rectory, Monsignor looked into the study where Father Dennis, who had finished confessions before him, was watching television.

Monsignor placed one hand on the door jamb and let it take his weight. "Who's got the sermon tomorrow?" he asked.

"Bob has."

"Tell him I'll take it." He turned away, then stopped and turned half way back. "And ask him to bring the announcement book up to my room." He ignored Father Dennis' amazed expression.

Upstairs, he climbed into his pajamas and then into bed. He picked up a book he had been reading but could not bring himself to open it. Lying there, he fiddled with one of the buttons on his silk pajama shirt, letting his mind wander. He wondered if the buttons were made so large to make it easier to operate them when you were tired. He remembered reading somewhere that if you were lost on the desert you could suck moisture out of a button. If that were true then, as buttons go, one of those on his pajama shirt would be equivalent to a tall glass of water.

Father Fonda rapped once and walked into Monsignor's room, surprising him with a button in his mouth. The only light came from the reading lamp over the bed, so that the tall, angular furniture stood in shadows along the walls, giving the room the look of a taxidermist's shop: a large wardrobe stood on its hind legs and a bureau moved stealthily along the wall, stalking a hassock. Father Fonda waved the announcement book in the air and dropped it on the foot of the bed. He walked across the room and fell heavily into the red leather chair and crossed his legs. The elastic of his white sweat socks was broken so that they sat in rings above his shoes like bracelets. Above the socks, his thick hairy legs gave no indication of tapering to ankles.

"You sure you want to take that sermon, Monsignor?"

"Of course I'm sure."

"I mean, I'm prepared and everything."

"You might knock on my door when you go down for the six," Monsignor said. "I don't trust this clock." He picked the clock up and turned it in his hand to see if anything had happened to make it trustworthy. As he set it down he sneaked a look at his palm, careful to keep the other hand closed, the finger tips touching the heel, making a nest.

"Okay, you're the boss," Father Fonda said. As he stood there was a sound like scotch tape being taken up. "You oughta cover this chair with something," he said, turning to look at it.

"I know. These hot nights it gets sticky."

"Not only that. It runs." He held out a beefy hand, palm up. "Look!"

Monsignor propped himself up on his elbows. "What's that?"

"I don' know. Dye, I guess. I hope I didn't get any on me." He grabbed a handful of his skirt and twisted around like a dog chasing its tail. "I guess not." He headed for the door. "Good night, Monsignor."

"Ah, wait a minute, Father."

Father Fonda stopped with his hand on the door and looked back to the bed where Monsignor had dropped back onto the pillows.

"Yes, Monsignor."

"You said you already prepared a sermon?"

"Sure. On matrimony."

Monsignor fingered his chin thoughtfully.

"Well, maybe you'd better take it then. As long as you're prepared."

"Whatever you say, Monsignor. You're the boss."

After Father Fonda had gone, Monsignor lay staring at the ceiling for several minutes. Finally he reached up and snapped off the light. Through the floor, he heard familiar music, then Marshal Dillon getting off a shot a split second late. Ten o'clock. He had been out of the confessional exactly one hour. He knew he would not go in again in his lifetime.

He shifted himself in the bed so that he would have the pleasure of settling into it again. He closed his eyes, then opened them. In the darkness he looked up at the ceiling.

"You're the boss," he said quietly. Then, quickly and without trying, in the way of children and old people, he went to sleep.

12. *OUR PARISH COUNCIL MEETS**

by Joel Wells

MINUTES OF THE FIRST MEETING OF THE
PARISH COUNCIL OF SAINT PROMETHEUS CHURCH

CONVENED AT 7:45 P.M. in the newly dedicated Parish
Council Assembly Room in the school basement (formerly
Brownies and paper drive storage). All officers of the executive
committee, members-at-large, designated and honorary members
were present with the exception of Mrs. Ronald Birkhoff (Liturgical Committee) whose husband called to say that she had dis-
located her hip at a Folk Mass.

Dr. Clive Barnes, president, called upon Msgr. George McMann
(Honorary Member) to give the opening prayer. Mr. Leslie
Porash (Christian Unity Committee) asked if it wouldn't be
better if the Council said the prayer as a body. Dr. Barnes told
Mr. Porash to sit down and shut up. Msgr. McMann said a prayer
to the Holy Spirit followed by an ejaculation to the Little Flower.
Mr. Porash said he didn't think the Council should pray to the
patron of docility. Dr. Barnes told Mr. Porash to shut up again.
Msgr. McMann said, no, it was all right, and that members of
the Council should feel free to speak their minds. Mr. Porash was

* From the April 1, 1968, issue of *Overview*.

probably right, he said, and it would be better if the Council prayed as a body in the future, provided they all knew the words, which he doubted. Dr. Barnes said that Msgr. had prepared a few remarks which he would like to read into the minutes. Mr. Porash said something which the recording secretary (me) missed. Msgr. McMann then read the following statement:

I have carried the load here at St. P's for thirty-three years now, and nobody can say that I've ever dragged my feet about making changes of any kind. I want to go on record as being 100 percent behind this parish council which is called for in the documents of Vatican II. We were the first parish in this part of town to get our altar turned around and while we're not the first parish to get our council on the tracks, we're not the last, by any means. So I'm just here to say that I welcome this opportunity to discuss things with you in an open, constructive way. But at the same time I've got to deal with the real nuts and bolts problems of keeping this big plant of ours humming. You make suggestions and go home, but your priests stay right here on the job twenty-four hours a day. As I said, I'm open to any reasonable suggestions, but I'd be letting you down and I'd be letting the bishop down if I wasted my time trying to implement every half-baked idea that came along. The Vatican Council made it clear that we're all laboring in the same vineyard, but a lot of people have taken that to mean that anybody is free to pick where he pleases. Well, Our Lord had something to say about that a long time before the Vatican Council. You all know the parable about the late-comers getting paid as much as the workers who had borne the heat of the day. Our Lord was upholding the management's right to ultimate authority there in no uncertain terms. Now I don't want you to defer to me just because I'm a priest of God and a Chamberlain to the Holy Father himself, but I do want you to remember that I'm your pastor. Now pastor means shepherd and a good shepherd has got to look out for the best interests of all his sheep. He can't think of only a few of them. That's about it. I want you to think of me as your shepherd and I'm here to tell you that this is one shepherd who's always willing to listen to his sheep.

Msgr. said that this concluded his remarks about policy and if anyone had any questions about it or anything else would they please make it snappy as he had an appointment with a contractor back at the rectory and would like to see the meeting adjourned by 8:15.

Mrs. Darcy (Education Committee) asked what it was that the Msgr. was going to talk to the contractor about as she wasn't about to authorize any building funds until the school library got a decent budget.

Dr. Barnes told Mrs. Darcy that it wasn't any of her business what the Msgr. talked to the contractor about and that she was only a designated member of the Council so she needn't think she was going to try and run the parish like she tried to run everybody else's business. Mrs. Darcy told Dr. Barnes that he ought to stick to what he knew best which was overcharging people for sloppy fillings and that she had every right to question the Msgr. The parish's money belonged to the People of God, she said, and even if she was just a designated member of the Council, she was still a full-fledged People of God.

Msgr. said that he was afraid that Mrs. Darcy hadn't paid much attention to his opening remarks. Questions like hers were obviously not in the spirit of Vatican II, he said, and she might do well to go home and read the Vatican documents and meditate on their meaning before she popped off to people.

Mrs. Darcy said that if that was the high-handed attitude he was going to take he'd better not look for much in the collection basket from the Darcy family to which Msgr. replied that he was glad she'd warned him or he would never have noticed the difference.

Mrs. Darcy left the meeting.

Dr. Barnes asked if there were any other questions before adjournment.

Mrs. George Petit (Social Life Committee) wondered if the Msgr. had reached any decision regarding the PTA's request that a sheltered bicycle rack be attached to the back wall of the rectory garage to keep the ice and snow off the children's bikes. Her own daughter, she said, had actually frozen to her bike seat just last week and had to be taken inside the house, bike and all, to thaw loose.

Msgr. said yes, he had reached a decision, and it was no. First of all, he said, the rectory garage was heated and this required a special kind of insulated siding which was easily cracked and the kids would undoubtedly ram their bikes into it. Secondly, he was not about to provide a convenient and hidden place right on the playground where the boys could smoke and commit other immoral acts; and thirdly, if Mrs. Petit would see to it that her daughter was modestly dressed it wouldn't be possible for her to freeze to her bike seat.

Mrs. Petit left the meeting.

Mr. Porash again said something which the secretary missed.

Dr. Barnes then thanked the Msgr. for sparing the Council so much of his time as we all understood that he was a very busy man. The Msgr. said it was his pleasure entirely and that any member of the Council should feel free to approach him at any time between meetings except on Wednesday which was his day off.

Dr. Barnes then asked for a motion to adjourn. Msgr. seconded.

13. ONE, HOLY, CATHOLIC AND WHITE*

Cartoons by Martin Murphy

"Good morning, my son! Good morning, my son!
Good morning, my son! Good morning, my boy!"

* From the February–March 1969 issue of *The Critic*.

"They'll change the water for us, won't they?"

"Ah-ha! I thought so!"

"Those little rascals certainly like to dress up, don't they?"

"This is our new church!"

"This is our power plant!"

"This is our new school!"

". . . And this is our Negro!"

"Oh my God! Guess who's coming to dinner?"

"Well, there goes the neighborhood!"

14. THE HIGHWAYMAN AND THE SAINT*

by Brian Friel

I NEVER REALLY hated Mrs. Wilson, Madge's mother. I
just thought of her as a bloody nuisance. But Madge hated her.
No sooner would we be settled down to a bit of courting on the
couch in the living room (and even though we were both in our
late thirties, we were eager enough) than the hand-bell would
ring, and Madge would mutter, "The old bitch!" and pull away
from me and dash up the stairs to see what the old woman
wanted this time. She never wanted anything, of course—Is the
fire safe? Was there a ring at the door? What time is it? She was
just making damn sure that Madge and I weren't going to enjoy
ourselves. For a time we thought it was the long silences that
made her suspicious, so Madge got me to recite poetry while we
courted; anything to make believe we were just chatting. I would
recite over and over again the only poem I learned at school,
The Highwayman by a poet called Alfred Noyes, and now and
again Madge would throw in something like, "It's a small world,
isn't it?" or "Just imagine. Fancy that." This worked fine as long

as I concentrated on what I was doing and not on what I was saying. I could rattle through the whole seventeen verses without a stop. But now and again a line would sound peculiar, and I would pause to wonder had I got it right, and then I would get stuck altogether, and before I would have time to go back to the beginning, "*The wind was a torrent of darkness among the gusty trees,*" the bell would go clang-clang-clang, and Madge would spit out a curse, and the session would be wrecked. I think, too, the old woman got cute to the poetry recitals because many a night, when I was rattling along at full steam, she would summon Madge. "We're like those Russian dogs that used to drivel!" Madge would say. It just goes to show that a man should never court a woman in her own house.

The trouble was that Mrs. Wilson was invalided with angina, and we couldn't very well go out and leave her alone. Cissy Cassidy, the next-door neighbor, kept an eye on her during the day, until Madge got home from the shirt factory at six. I came round about seven (I'm a joiner in the Acme Furniture Company) and stayed until bedtime. Apart from the bell-ringing and Madge's tempers I suppose it wasn't a bad way to spend the nights. It meant that I could save my wages and put down a deposit on a house in Riverview for ourselves, and anyhow we wouldn't have been going to dances or films because the old man wasn't long dead. I had met him a few times. He was average height, about the same build as myself, and a quieter or more civil man never walked. He was a stoker in St. Patrick's hospital, and the heat of the furnace must have dried him out because he was as yellow as a duck's foot. He had the longest chin you ever saw and he was so shy about it that he had it pulled away back into his throat. This meant that his cheeks and his mouth were always lined, as if he were smiling, and that he looked at you from under his forehead. Madge inherited her chin from him, but in those days hers was stuck out, aggressive, like an amateur boxer's, and it got red and shiny every time the bell rang. The old man worked night shifts, and the only times I met him were

on Sunday afternoons. He would sit in the back garden with a
big book about birds on his knees and binoculars up to his face
and watch the hedge sparrows hopping about the wall at the end
of the yard. I used to wonder what he needed the binoculars for
because the wall was five yards from where he sat. Maybe he
thought they hid him; or maybe he knew you don't like inter-
rupting a man with binoculars. Anyhow, we never had any conversation beyond "Good evening, Mr. Wilson" and "Oh, hello,
Andy." He dropped dead in the basement of the hospital with a
coal shovel in his hand, and when they laid him out, his chin
stuck up so far above the sides of the coffin that they had to
open his mouth to get the lid on. When she saw him gaping
savagely up at her—I can tell you I got a bit of a fright myself
—Mrs. Wilson collapsed. She was ordered to bed and never,
except on one occasion, got out of it again.

Her bedroom was a sight. The bedside table was covered with
medicines, and the walls were covered with holy pictures, and
beside her on the pillow where Mr. Wilson's head used to rest—
Madge said he chose night shifts to avoid his wife—lay the big
brass hand-bell. It had belonged to Mrs. Wilson's grandfather,
Flames Flaherty, who used to run before the fire brigade in the
old days, clearing the streets; or so Cissy Cassidy told me. But
the most important thing in the room was the shrine. It was really
a chest of drawers completely covered by a white sheet, and it
looked like an altar in a church. At the ends were two lit candles
and at the front a vase of artificial flowers and in the centre was
the statue of Saint Philomena.

Saint Philomena was a blue and gold and white girl, with a
long graceful frock that touched the top of her bare feet. Her
hair fell to her waist, and her arms were folded across her chest,
and she held her head to the side as if she were listening for
something. Mrs. Wilson had a habit of punctuating her prayers
with deep satisfied sighs, and every time she did this, the candles
flickered, and whatever way the shadows shifted, you would
imagine Saint Philomena lifted her face a little bit higher. As the

rosary rolled on and on, I used to think that she was Bess, the landlord's black-eyed daughter in my poem, waiting for the highwayman to come riding across the purple moor; or that she was Mrs. Wilson, listening for the creaking of the springs in the living room couch; or that she was Madge, cocking her ear for the hand-bell, although how I ever saw any resemblance between this good-looking girl and Madge I can't imagine now. Anyhow, between Bess and Mrs. Wilson and Madge, I didn't pray much.

The prayers began every night on the stroke of ten. As soon as the big bell would ring, Madge would shout up to the ceiling, "Coming!" and then fix her hair and her clothes, and we would go up together to the bedroom. Mrs. Wilson was such a wee fairy of a woman that you would scarcely notice her in the huge bed. The first thing you would see were the two big soft innocent eyes, then the round white face, then the tiny hands lying patiently on top of the counterpane. She never raised her voice above a whisper even though she opened her mouth as if she were eating a juicy pear. She always addressed me as Thomas (I was christened Thomas Andrew) although everybody in Omagh knows me as Andy.

"Good evening, Thomas," she would whisper. "Are you going to join in the family rosary?" As if I had come up to play poker!

"Yes, Mrs. Wilson."

"Good boy. Good boy. Madge, fix my head so that I can see Saint Philomena."

Madge, leading with her chin, would stuff the pillows behind her back as if she were punishing them.

"Lovely. Thank you," the old woman would say. "It's so nice for me to have you both kneeling at my bedside. As Father Peyton says, 'The family that prays together stays together.' "

"Get on with the rosary!" Madge would snap.

"And Father Peyton's right, isn't he, Thomas?"

"Yes, Mrs. Wilson," I would say, avoiding Madge's wild eyes.

"Indeed he is. I'm so lucky to have you both." Then, to the statue, "Thank you, Saint Philomena."

I could see that she was as crafty as hell, playing Madge and me and Father Peyton and Saint Philomena against one another, but somehow I could never get angry with her. Maybe that was because Madge had enough anger for the two of us. But for no good reason at all I began to hate Father Peyton and Saint Philomena. I felt that they were responsible for all our troubles. Here I was, not as young as I might have been, with a house ready to step into and a woman ready to marry me; and there was Father Peyton and Saint Philomena coming between me and a normal life—just because I was civil enough to join in the rosary every night. As if things weren't awkward enough for us without making them permanently awkward by praying together! It amounted to this: every time I got down on my knees in that bedroom I cut my own throat.

After the rosary Madge and I would go down to the kitchen for supper. The prayers always seemed to knock any notion of courting out of our heads. We would sit there at the table and talk listlessly about our problem.

"We could take her with us to Riverview," I would begin.

"Not bloody likely! Besides, she would never leave this house."

"What about getting her into St. Patrick's?"

"She's not sick enough. They have no spare beds for cranks."

"The Nazareth nuns would take her into their Home. If she sold this house and brought the money with her, they would be damn glad to welcome her."

"She wouldn't go to them above all people."

"Well, what are we going to do? She's your mother."

"I don't know, Andy. Honest to God, I just don't know."

"You don't expect me to come in here, do you?" I would say, thinking of Saint Philomena and Father Peyton and getting annoyed. "I mean to say, leaping into the air every time you hear that bloody bell isn't my idea of married life! By God, you don't expect that of me, do you?"

Sometimes her eyes would flash with anger and she would say, "The old bitch! I'll tell her tomorrow that we're going to clear

out, and she can damn well forage for herself!" Sometimes she
would just sit there and cry, big big chin quivering. And sometimes she would fling her arms around me and kiss my ears and
my neck, and I would have to plunge into *The Highwayman,* in
the excitement sometimes beginning at Part Two, "*He did not
come in the dawning; he did not come at noon.*" Sudden courting
like that was the sweetest of all. I would forget altogether the
bloody mess we were in.

It was the Acme Furniture Company that finally pushed us into
marriage. They landed a big contract to fit out a new hotel that
was being built near Belfast airport, and all the unmarried car-
penters in the firm were being sent off on the eighteen-month job.
I explained the situation to Madge. It was now or never, I said.
She didn't hesitate for a second.

"We'll get married next Wednesday!" she said.

"What about the old woman?"

"We'll worry about that afterwards."

"And we'll live in Riverview?"

"Andy," she said, smiling up at me, "I love you that much I
could eat you!"

We didn't get married that Wednesday because Cissy Cassidy
had the flu and there would have been no one to look in on the
old woman, but we got married the following Saturday. Immediately after the ceremony we came back to the house to see her.
She cried her eyes out with happiness. So did Madge. They held
on to one another and laughed and cried, and I stood there
beside the altar, grinning, all stiff in my new suit, like a bloody
fool. Mrs. Wilson's mouth kept opening wide but not even a
whisper came. Her big innocent eyes were on Saint Philomena,
and I believe she was mouthing Thank you, Thank you. Then,
she signalled for Madge and me to get down on our knees beside
her and she joined her hands and said some sort of a prayer over
us, and Madge and she hugged one another again, and we were
all so happy that I stepped forward like a man and kissed the

old woman on the forehead. Maybe I cried, too; I don't remember. Anyhow, we got away eventually and took the bus to Portrush where we stayed in the Grand Hotel until Monday morning.

The biggest mistake I made was to go back to the house after the honeymoon even for a week, until the painters were finished in Riverview. Because the week stretched into two, and then into a month, and then into three months, and then the old woman got a chill, and then it was Christmas, and finally Madge said one night that since furnished houses were fetching such high prices we should let Riverview.

"What the hell do you mean?" I said.

"It's pointless having it idle, isn't it?" she said, tilting up the chin.

"It shouldn't be idle," I said. "We should be in it."

"And what about mother?" There wasn't so much of the 'old bitch' now."

"She's welcome to come with us. And well she knows it. And well you know it."

"I'll tell you what, Andy. We'll leave here in the spring. The evenings will be longer, and it won't be so lonely for her. Just wait another two months."

"You've given me time limits before."

"I mean it. Honest to God, I do. The spring, and that's the end."

I think she really did mean it.

"Is that a promise, Madge?"

But then the hand-bell rang, and she said, "The old bitch!" the way she used to say it; only I got the notion she said it just to please me. Anyhow, she ran away upstairs without promising.

And that was the funny thing about the bell-ringing now. Before we were married the old woman always rang it when there was a silence downstairs. Now we might sit in the living room for a whole night without speaking a word to one another, and there would never be a tinkle from the bedroom. But as soon as we would start chatting, the clang-clang-clang would waken the dead; you would swear the town was on fire. Another difference in our lives was that I stopped going up for prayers at night. Madge didn't speak to me for a week when I stalled first, and for the most of that time I didn't even know she wasn't speaking to me, not until she told me. But as I explained to her, why should I pray together when staying together was the last thing in the world I wanted? She accused me then of flying in the face of providence, and I pointed out that it wasn't providence I was up in arms against but Father Peyton and Saint Philomena, the Terrible Twins, as I called them. Only for them, I said, the old woman wouldn't have a leg to stand on. I can tell you that brought the color to her chin!

It's funny, too, how things turn out. If Madge hadn't forgotten to put my lunch-box in my coat pocket that day, I wouldn't have gone to the works canteen; and if I hadn't gone to the canteen, I might never have known of the Vatican announcement. Anyhow, there I was, sitting beside George Williamson, eating my lunch, and not thinking about anything in particular. All I knew about Williamson was that he was a French polisher in the finishing department and a bitter black Protestant.

"D'you see this?" he said, reaching over the paper he was reading.

"What's that?" I said.

"It would appear," he said, smirking, "that the Pope isn't infallible after all. Now, isn't that a terrible shock?"

"I don't know what you're talking about, mate," I said.

"It's in the paper here," he said. "Look, man. Read it for yourself. 'The Saint That Never Was. Saint Philomena Is Pushed From Her Pedestal.' "

At the mention of Saint Philomena, I snatched the paper from his hands and read through the news item. My God, he was telling the truth! Official Vatican sources today announced, the paper said, that the devotion of all Roman Catholics to Saint Philomena must be discontinued because there is little or no evidence that this person ever existed. I didn't trouble to read any more. All that mattered was that Saint Philomena was no more a saint than my granny was. And with her out of the way, Father Peyton was a pushover!

"Williamson," I said, slapping him across the back, "may you never know want or discomfort, and may all your dreams come true!" And ignoring his calls to me to give him back his paper, I skipped out of the canteen like a ten-year-old. I think that was the happiest moment of my life.

I shouldn't have got drunk after work. That's what spoiled everything. I should have nursed my news and gloated over it and chuckled privately about it. But I went and got plastered and then, singing "God Save Ireland," I marched to the house and straight up to the old woman's bedroom. I threw the paper at the old woman and said, "There's something for you to read." But I was more interested in Saint Philomena than in the old woman. I caught the statue and held it above my head and went waltzing around the room, reciting the fifteenth verse of *The Highwayman* at the top of my voice: *"Back, he spurred like a madman, shrieking a curse to the sky, / With the white road smoking behind him, and his rapier brandished high! / Blood-red were his spurs i' the golden noon, wine-red was his velvet coat, / When they shot him down on the highway, / Down like a dog on the highway, / And he lay in his blood on the highway, with a bunch of lace at his throat."*

Then all hell broke loose: the old woman screaming and ringing the bell; Madge roaring at me and trying to console her mother at the same time; Cissy Cassidy pounding on the front door to know what was wrong. Still reciting, I went down and opened the door for her. She gave me a quick look and shot past me. I swaggered into the kitchen and put on a kettle for tea and went back out to the foot of the stairs and shouted up, "Yo-ho! Yo-ho! The family that thinks together drinks together!" or some silly nonsense like that. I went into the living room and bounced up and down on the couch until the springs hummed. "Listen!" I called up to the ceiling. "Do you hear? Can you hear me, Philomena?" Then I went back to the kitchen and set the table for

myself and sang hymns and ate a bloody big tea. My God, I felt
like a king! I must have fallen asleep after that because the next
thing I remember is waking up at 1:00 A.M. and trying to piece
together what had happened. I had a very sore head.

The house was as still as a graveyard. I tiptoed upstairs and
looked into our bedroom. Madge wasn't there. I went into the
old woman's bedroom. The bed was empty! The bell was there
on the pillow, and the candles were lit in the altar, but the old
woman and the statue were gone. Holy God, had I killed the
old woman! I can tell you the sweat broke on me then. I dashed
downstairs and just as I got to the bottom, the front door opened.

Cissy Cassidy came in first. So that was where they were—
next door. Then came Mrs. Wilson. She was wearing a coat over
her nightdress, and her face was white and sad and holy looking.
Madge was last, her arm around the old woman in support. None
of them said a word. The three of them just walked past me
and up the stairs, as if I weren't there. I tried to look into Madge's
face, but she kept her eyes on the ground, and her chin, I noticed,
looked as if it were polished. I went into the living room and
sat on the edge of a seat, like in the old days when I was waiting
for Madge. But now I was the one that was doing the listening,
trying to pick up any sound from the bedroom above. I could
hear nothing.

In the end I could stick the silence no longer. I had to go up.
As soon as I entered, they began the rosary. The old woman was
in the bed, propped up with pillows, facing the altar, Madge was
kneeling beside the bed, Cissy near the door. I knelt down beside
Cissy. Madge and her mother prayed with their eyes closed.
They did a lot of sighing.

"God forgive you for this night's work," Cissy hissed to me.

"Shut up!" I hissed back.

"Depriving the poor woman of the saint of her life."

"Don't blame me. Blame the Pope."

"But you'll not steal the next one from her. Because you'll
never be told who she is. And we've decided not even to have
a statue."

"What are you talking about?"

"She has fixed on another saint—in place of Saint Philomena."

"Who?"

"That's something you'll never know. Never!"

"What d'you mean?"

"Wild horses wouldn't drag that information out of us. You'll never know who you're praying to. You'll do no more damage." Madge heard us whispering. She glanced across at us. And as she did, I noticed that her chin was no longer thrust out aggressively but was withdrawn into her neck so that her cheeks and her mouth were lined in a fixed sad smile. Then, her eyes glided back to the altar, and from under her forehead she stared dreamily at the space between the two lit candles.

I have a good tenant in Riverview. He pays me regularly on the first Saturday of every month. Occasionally I walk over there and take a look at the outside of the house: he has rose trees in the front and a vegetable plot in the back. It looks very cosy. But by the time you get home from work and get washed, you don't feel like going out much. So, if the weather is good, I usually sit out in the back garden and watch the hedge sparrows through the old man's binoculars. Then, when the bell rings, I go up to the old woman's bedroom for the rosary. Madge sleeps there now, ever since that night, just in case the old woman might get an attack. Not that that's likely; the doctor says she'll outlive us all. And her mind's as clear as ever. When I go into the room, she whispers, "Good evening, Thomas. Are you going to join in the family rosary?" and then she smiles over at the candles and the artificial flowers, and you can see her lips saying Thank you, Thank you. Of course, she never drops even a hint of who her new saint is. Indeed, she has got so crafty she doesn't even mention Father Peyton's name. All she says is, "It's so nice for me to have you both kneeling at my bedside. As a certain American priest says, 'The family that prays together stays together.' " By God, you've got to admire the old bitch! She could handle a regiment.

15. *THE SUBMERGING LAYMAN**

by Thomas Edwards

THIS IS AN examination of conscience. Ask yourself the questions in private. Answer honestly. This quiz may change your entire life. (See answers and analysis pp. 123-125.)

Quiz

1. Can you remember the words to the first verse of the *Tantum Ergo* . . . in Latin?
2. When the Gospel about the 200 *denarii* is read, only they don't say *denarii* but instead 200 *days work*, do you secretly become angry?
3. When the priest tells you the reason the word *denarii* is not used any longer is because people understand 200 *days work* better than *denarii*, does your anger turn to latent hostility?
4. Do you know what the words "The Lord Be With You" mean in Latin?
5. Have you at any time within the past six months carried a rosary in your pocket, even on airplane flights?
6. When someone comes up to you at a cocktail party and tells

---

* From the June–July 1966 issue of *The Critic*.

you that God is dead, do you have a secret urge to punch him in the mouth?

7. If the person who tells you that God is dead happens to be a Catholic, do you in fact punch him in the mouth?

8. Can you adequately define a novena, Benediction, Forty Hours?

9. Do you stand or sit silently while the rest of the congregation is singing hymns with great gusto, off-key, and two measures ahead of the organist?

10. When someone mentions the dynamism of the New Breed, do your thoughts immediately turn to Herefords, Shetlands, and Schnauzers?

If you are a Catholic, between the ages of eighteen and sixty-five, and if you have answered "yes" to six or more of the questions at left, you obviously have a major problem. Therapy to correct the fault is helpful, but many of those suffering the malady often turn to their parish priest. This presents an additional problem because he is often booked up months in advance, what with Urban League, B'nai B'rith, and National Council of Churches meetings, plus CFM, YCS, CCD, and all the other acronymous groups to which he must tend. Often by the time an appointment is made, the layman-patient (or patient layman) has totally submerged and is beyond all help. Rather than seek out your confessor (he's the one who used to be located in those dandy little offices at the side of Church which are now being used to store the hymn cards), study the actions listed below. If you don't agree with them, change them. After all, that's what Renewal is for, isn't it?

1. The *Tantum Ergo* syndrome is one which, happily, is dying out throughout most of this country. The last reported public case of any consequence was in Sheboygan where a thirty-two-year-old male was repeatedly found in the rear of the Church at the end of Sunday Mass saying in a loud, clear voice the word "Amen," using the soft "A" as in "Aw, Father, he's not heavy, he's my

brother." Concerted efforts were made to have this individual switch to the harder "Amen" as in "Up, up and *aw*ay." The efforts were unsuccessful. An intensive study was made into his background and the origin of the flaw was traced back to the man's childhood where it was found he had viewed *Going My Way* a total of twenty-two times. Unfortunately, before treatment could begin, the man left Sheboygan to study in Italy under an Ottaviani fellowship.

2. The question of *denarii* has been raised quite often. What the layman must remember is that *denarii* is an outmoded term for the currency present at the time of Christ. A change was needed to update the translation. A common question asked on this is, "Why didn't they just say dollars?" Such a question shows the utter ignorance of the questioner for we surely had to have a universal term—not just one for this country—hence, not dollars, pounds, yen, drachmas, rubles, etc. Instead we now talk about 200 *days work*. What's that? You say that 200 days work may mean a new car for one man, a pair of shoes for another, a loaf of bread for a third. Next question (smart aleck).

3. Now, really, you shouldn't get that disturbed when the priest tries to explain the changes to you. He's your spiritual leader, your brother, and he's anxious to have you adapt to changes OR ELSE.

4. Similar to the *Tantum Ergo* syndrome with one slight difference. Everyone knew *Dominus Vobiscum* (wash our mouth out) even in the Old Church. It is extremely difficult not to remember this one. But, next year you had better shape up, fellow.

5. If you answered "yes" to this one, what can we say. What are you, some kind of nut on symbolism or something? Don't you know that superstition is out? Oh, you're a nun. Well, Sister, you don't have any business taking this quiz anyway.

6. What are you trying to do, impede the whole ecumenical movement? That fellow has a right to his opinions. You must enter into dialogue with him, and make that commitment so that you can witness and have your encounter. He may be right and we may as well hedge our bets.

7. And that goes for your Catholic brethren, too.

8. The only cure for this is to repeat very slowly the following words whenever you think of any such things. "SEE - JUDGE - ACT." Once more, now—"See - Judge - Act." I think you've got it.

9. Horrendous. What really counts, man, is that you participate. So what if you don't know the words, or like them, or can't carry a tune. You're participating when you sing and that's what matters. Don't just sit there praying, ACT!

10. I don't think you're really trying. Don't you realize that the New Breed are those young priests who are doing all of the wonderful things for the New Church, like organizing unions for priests (oops, sorry about that, Bishop). Get with it.

There you have it. If your "yeses" point you out to be a submerging layman, bear up. You can still be saved and be a part of the dynamic Church, your Church. Who knows, someday you may emerge. You may someday be dedicated and won't have to waste all your time praying silently and things like that.

16. THE LIFE AND TIMES OF ST. FIDGETA*

by John Bellairs

IN 482 A.D., St. Fidgeta was born of Christian parents in the little village of Stercoraria in Southern Gaul. Her life, like that of most of the people who lived in the fifth century A.D., was rather dull until her parents were overrun by a foraging band of Avars. Fidgeta was left in the care of her pagan uncle, Leitotes, who sent her to a pagan grammar school where almost every day the sacred mysteries of her religion were held up to ridicule. Her teacher, the notorious skeptic Putricordes, would frequently quote from Porphyry's now lost attack on Christianity. It is through her faithful, if reluctant, note-taking that the only known fragment of this odious work has been passed down to us. A wax tablet (preserved in the convent of the Fidgettines in Fobbio) bears her name and "JMJ" at the top, and has farther down the page a note, which is labeled "Jocus Porphyris." A rough translation of the corrupt Late Latin would run thus:

Q. Why does a Christian cross himself?
A. To get to the other side.

* Subsequently appeared in *St. Fidgeta & Other Parodies* by John Bellairs. Copyright © 1966 by John Bellairs. Reprinted by permission of The Macmillan Company.

Scholars agree that the joke seems to lose something in translation.

Despite her diligence, Fidgeta crossed the pagan teacher constantly. During workshop, she would string rosaries or plait penitential whips; throughout the morning idolatry sessions, she would fidget ceaselessly and mumble forbidden prayers. Once she was even caught with an inkwell full of holy water. Finally, during a Sunday morning class in March of 489, she fidgeted so much in her desire to go to Mass that the distraught pedagogue slapped her to death. She was canonized in 490, after having cured Zephyrinus the Anchorite of the nervous shakes.

Facts About St. Fidgeta

St. Fidgeta is the patroness of nervous and unmanageable children. Her shrine is the Church of Santa Fidgeta in Tormento, near Fobbio in southern Italy. There one may see the miraculous statue of St. Fidgeta, attributed to the Catholic Casting company of Chicago, Illinois. This statue has been seen to squirm noticeably on her feastday, and so on that day restless children from all over Europe have been dragged to the shrine by equally nervous, worn-out, and half-mad parents. Though no diminution of fidgeting has been noticed in these children, the feeling is that at least the restlessness will be converted into meritorious work by the action of the saint. On this point see Tertullian, who proves that fidgeting is (or can be) useful unto salvation. Also, see Gregory of Mopsuhestia, on fidgeting as a prelude to mystical experience.

The Fidgettines

The Church of Santa Fidgeta in Tormento was built on the spot where the saint appeared in 1272 to Scintilla Sforza, who became Mother Latifundia, foundress of the order of Faithful Fidgettines (O.F.F.). Scintilla, before her vision a spendthrift of checkered reputation, notorious for her midnight levées in the ruins of the

Golden House of Nero, was so moved by the miraculous experience that she forsook all earthly joys and wrung from her father, a rich Florentine banker, the 800 acre tract on which she built the first Fidgettine convent. This fortress of virtue crowns a high hill near Fobbio, and today visitors may inspect its 18-foot-thick walls, its crenellated towers, and its now empty cannon embrasures. On the hillside below, happy tenant farmers work the vast Fidgettine estate as they have for years, though the sisters have now moved to a new chrome and glass high-rise convent built for them by a Sicilian charitable organization.

The order flourished and spread under the guidance of its patroness, and the following saints stud its history like jewels of lambent flame.

St. Pudibunda, who on her wedding night decided that God had called her to a life of spotless virginity. The causes of her death that very night are not known, but the pious may guess at them. She was posthumously admitted to the order.

St. Adiposa, author of numerous anti-ascetic tracts. She decided that a life intentionally cut short by overweight could be consecrated to God. Confined to her cell by immobility for much of her life, she wrote a long, strangely moving hymn to St. Fidgeta in which the saint is compared to a peach, a plum, a whortleberry, and various other comestibles. The last few stanzas, written in the author's old age, show signs of creative degeneration and are usually omitted.[1] They compare St. Fidgeta to a sugar cone, a bonbon, and finally, to a squab:

> Browned in the oven of the Father's Light,
> Stuffed with grace and with sage advice.

St. Adiposa died at ninety-three when the floor of her cell collapsed. Her life-principle of caloric immolation caused much

---

[1] Professor Schweigermutter disagrees in his *Das Fidgetaslied und der Deutsche Geist* (Lüneberg, 1872), 16 vols. He regards these verses as the culmination of metaphysical imagery.

debate about her status as a martyr. The Council of Trent shelved the matter, and there it stands.

St. Dragomira, the warrior nun of Bosnia. Converted from paganism by the Fidgettine missionary Anfractua, she spent her life in fomenting religious wars, and is usually credited with Christianizing Upper Bosnia. She was clubbed to death by her pagan brother, Bogeslaw, after a long and heated argument about Christian hate. Patroness of edged weapons.

St. Fidgeta in Art

St. Fidgeta's symbols in art are the red slap-mark on the cheek, the scholar's pen, and the virgin's girdle. Early representations of her are rare, since the stasis of Byzantine art does not permit the depiction of a restless saint. There may, however, have been an icon of St. Fidgeta in the monastery of the Studium in Constantinople. On the other hand, there may not have been. But if it did exist, it was probably destroyed when Isaac Comnenus smashed the furnishings of the Studium and made his half-brother Dropsus eat the pieces.

Be that as it may, some art historians interpret the Renaissance struggle for motion in art as an attempt to depict St. Fidgeta. In Baroque art she received her best treatment, especially in the "Apotheosis of St. Fidgeta," by Rubens, which was once the altarpiece of Santa Fidgeta in Tormento. The painting was hidden during the Allied invasion of Italy in World War II, and is thought to be still camouflaged as a Coca-Cola sign.

Other famous representations are Caravaggio's "St. Fidgeta Chastised by St. Jerome" and Fragonard's "Sainte Fidgeta dans l'extase."[2]

---

[2] Professor Schlechty, in his *Fragonard's Fidgetabild und Romantische Weltschmerz* (München, 1892), complains of the impropriety of having cupids pinching and tickling the saint. Sister Regina Coeli Laetare, O.F.F., in her *Fidgeta and the Problem of the Catholic Artist in an Altogether Too Secularized Society* (Altoona, 1932), retorts hotly that the cupids are allegorical.

Miracles of St. Fidgeta

No account of this saint's life would be complete without mention of some of her more remarkable apparitions and miraculous feats. Most famous is the routing of the Turkish siege of Pinsk in 1450, when St. Fidgeta appeared in a fluffy pink cloud on the walls of the city and, stretching forth a chubby hand, induced in the heathen army a state of uneasiness that soon reduced the soldiers of the Prophet to nerveless idiocy. In 658, the Persian Emperor Tissaphernes led his mighty host against the Byzantine city of Ud. But on the evening before a decisive battle, he retired to his tent with an unaccountable feeling of disquietude. He awoke in the night with a tiny voice in his ear saying, "tickle, tickle," and soon was rolling on the ground in shrieking convulsions of laughter. His army fled in terror.

Naturally, there are many tales of miraculous cures attributed to St. Fidgeta. Children afflicted with incurable cases of diaper rash, itchy thumb, sweaty palms, and general fussing, have been cured overnight when their distressed mothers prayed to the tiny saint. One such case is documented by a letter to the "Catholic Problems" column of the *Sunday Intruder*:

Dear Father Thurifer:

My six-year-old daughter Eudoxia was a chronic fidgeter. She twitched and fiddled endlessly during Mass, much to the consternation of myself and my husband Voltimand, who holds the consecutive Communions record at St. Ogmus Parish. I tried everything to make her stop. I made 92 First Fridays, 56 First Saturdays, and 12 First Mondays, if there is such a thing, though I think my son Caxton made it up. I got calluses on my thumb from rosaries and sprained my index finger turning on electric vigil lights, even though Father Usk is stingy and turns them off every night. (Not that I mean any disrespect toward the clergy, of course. I just mean he knows a nickel when he sees one, ha, ha.) Anyway, I finally prayed to St. Fidgeta and my daughter stopped fidgeting. Once a week though she has what our family calls the screaming woo-hoos. Is there any saint for that?

Mrs. Emily Faldstool

Father Thurifer's answer, which need not be quoted in full here, indicates that the child's seizures are some variety of stigmata, and should go away after a while.

Another letter from the *Intruder*:

Dear Father Plotch:
My son used to break into uncontrollable laughter during the Last Gospel. He says that one Sunday when this happened a little girl with frizzy blond hair in the pew ahead of him said she would give him a fat lip if he didn't stop. After Mass we waited outside and no little blond girl came out. We think it was St. Fidgeta.
Mrs. Anthony Adverse Crapple

Finally, we ought to note the cause of the little girl in the English village of Retching-under-Tweed who saw a mysterious light in the village chapel one night. She was not suffering from anything, nor did she ever see anything unusual again, but it was discovered that the chapel is only 40 miles from the site of a medieval Fidgettine (or perhaps Saxifragian) convent.

The St. Fidgeta Devotional

ST. ADIPOSA'S PRAYER FOR RELIEF OF UNEASINESS
(effective within 24 hours)
O Sweet Fidgeta, tiniest candle on the sugar cake of Eternity, grant that my nervousness may be seared away by thy honeyed flame, or that it may at least be made useful, till I have passed through the stomach of life . . . (Here several words are blotted out, and the prayer seems never to have been finished.)

PRAYER AGAINST ENEMIES *(attributed to St. Dragomira)*
O Fidgeta, who dost cause the unrighteous to scratch where it does not itch, grant that the hateful N. may be afflicted with tickles, the stitch, the cramp, underarm rash, prickly foot, and all manner of unexplained twinges.

The Litany of St. Fidgeta

(*to be chanted by children ages 3–12*)

Quieter of the giggly
Steadier of the wiggly
Calmer of the tickly
Soother of the prickly

*Teach us to
sit still*

From woolen shirts, squeaky corduroy
and metal laundry tags . . .

From the unaccountable feeling that we
can see our noses and that it will
make us cross-eyed . . .

From feet that go to sleep and will almost
certainly develop gangrene . . .

From the feeling that during the night we
will contract leprosy and our toes will
drop off . . .

From the fear that also during the night the
Communists will crawl over the window
sill and take over and we will have the
strength to die for our Faith . . .

From nuns who describe exactly what the
Indians did to St. Isaac Jogues and his
friends . . .

From demonic possession, scabby knees,
and all causes of the desire to itch,
twitch, or run screaming up and down . . .

*Sweet Fidgeta,
steer us clear!*

17. *DIALOGUE WITH MYSELF**

by Lucile Hasley

HOW, I WONDER, does one start a schism? I feel pretty silly, not even knowing the first step, but I give it to you straight: it simply was *not* included in my convert instructions. So chalk up another black mark, please, against our outmoded seminaries. Imagine! Letting a convert sally forth into the world without this basic safeguard against a rainy day!

Still, as an emerging layman with both feet firmly planted in mid-air, I naturally want to do my part—that is, participating to the fullest in Mother Church's present upheaval and confusion —and I felt that a modest little schism would not go unappreciated. It seems that I don't qualify as a would-be heretic (quote: "The theologically untutored don't know enough theology to be guilty of heresy") but must leave this to the speculative theologians. I don't mind—they seem to be doing a good job of it— but surely any layman, with enough git-up-and-go, can start a schism, no matter how amateurish.

What I had in mind . . . well, I feel that a schism, to be respectable, should be over a fairly large issue (no small potatoes like "Down With Hymn-Singing") and yet not so drastic as to

* From the February–March 1966 issue of *The Critic*.

cause any hard feelings. Not ecumenical. I'd be satisfied, really, with just a small paragraph in some future Catholic Encyclopedia. Something like: "Legend has it that the Hasley Schism, started by a housewife in South Bend, Indiana, soon spread to Asia Minor. Centuries later, her position vindicated by Rome, one of Mrs. Hasley's bones (the ulna, it is believed) is now one of the most revered relics in the Sistine Chapel."

That's modest enough, surely. But how do I get going? I don't want to tack up a proclamation on a church door (that's been done) or try anything so flamboyant as sky-writing over the Notre Dame stadium or anything so proasic as ringing doorbells or . . .

"How," I asked my husband, "do you start a schism?"

He put down his newspaper. He looked thoughtful. "Well, it seems to me," he said, "that the first thing is to learn how to pronounce it."

I practiced for a full week—trying to get the "siz" sound instead of the "ch"—and then gave up. Maybe I just lack the necessary leadership, I don't know. Still, my "followship" doesn't seem too good, either. Finally, I said to myself, "Oh, rats." (I still cling to the old habit of ejaculations.) "Oh, rats," I said. "Well, I can at least write another dialogue to add to the pile."

That's right: dialogue. To call this a monologue would imply there's only one of me, muttering to myself, whereas I really have two Luciles to contend with. One of me goes under the label of "emerging layman" (here, picture an ape-like creature—emerging from the primordial slime—who is just learning to walk on her two hind legs instead of on all fours) and was created, I think, by the Catholic press.

It is alleged that, prior to the Council, this wretched creature (who only emerged from her "ghetto" when she had to catch a non-Catholic train or something) sat like a wooden Indian in her pew; occasionally rattling her rosary on major feast days but mainly passing the time in a dead stupor. The priest, for all she knew, might have been an ancient Druid mumbling incantations over a cauldron of simmering toads, newts, and bats.

Then came the vernacular! Our wretched layman is stunned: so *this* is what the Mass is all about? Fancy! Next, for the very first time, our layman hears a brand new phrase: Mystical Body. Do tell! And what's all this inflammatory talk about treating your neighbor—be he Jew, Negro, or Protestant—as a human being? Our emerging layman, blinded by this new vision, totters weakly down the church steps and into the big bad secular world. . . .

Now the other Lucile (a strong-minded and eccentric old biddy) keeps insisting she "emerged" exactly thirty-five years ago, when she joined the Church, and that no one is going to talk her out of it. Oddly enough, she even claims that she was exposed to the Golden Rule message while still a Presbyterian, that she always assumed this was pretty basic to Christianity, and looked to the Catholic Church for something above and beyond the humanitarian: some supernatural truths, as it were, to speed the Good Samaritan on his way.

This same Lucile (I forgot to mention that she's also a sentimental slob) keeps pointing to her wrists—bearing no cruel and ugly chain marks—and trying to bear witness that, honestly, Mother Church has treated her quite decently over the years. And since she never thought of the Church as another Alcatraz, she can't get it through her thick skull that now, and only now, is she free to think, and move, and speak. Neither can she believe that the "erring" Church, sitting in Council, has *just* discovered that love makes the world go round. Moreover, she always thought that love of neighbor was something you had to work at all your life; not something that went into effect, overnight, like a new Church ruling on fasting.

Hence, she just hasn't the heart to join the others as they jubilantly dance, and chant, around the body of the dear departed: the institutional Church. Is there no one, she wonders, who loved the old girl? (They used to say they'd *die* for her.) No one to shed a nostalgic tear at her passing; admit that, beneath the encrustations, she couldn't have been ALL bad?

Or, is everyone so anxious to be considered avant garde these

days that they don't *dare* betray any lingering affection? Or, for
that matter, any lingering common sense?

The early apostles would be proud of us: accepting every theological rumor, no matter how wild, rather than be caught with
our "old guard" petticoat showing. The Pope, poor man, has asked
the faithful to suspend judgment but many of the faithful, unquote,
would rather hear the cock crow, for the third time, than hear
their neighbor crow. ("You mean you still believe in the virgin
birth? Dear girl, where *have* you been?")

Really, if someone at a cocktail party casually mentioned that
the Trinity has now been discarded, I doubt if anyone would admit
surprise. A few martinis might halt in mid-air, temporarily, or be
hastily gulped, but the avant garders would rally: "But of course!
I believe that was in last week's *Time*, wasn't it? Or am I con-
fusing this with the 'God is dead' school? Anyway, we've naturally
seen this coming."

The really clever way to fence, though, is to parry a question
with a question. If questioned, say, about the divinity of Christ,
you should say thoughtfully: "Well, now, let's define our terms.
What do you mean by the word 'divinity'? What do you mean by
the word 'Christ'?"

But let us return to that lovable character, the emerging layman,
who not only doesn't read *Time* but, apparently, doesn't even read
English.

Priests seem very fond of this character: pure virgin mission
territory. They seem not so fond of characters like me. I have
been ruined, they fear, by the superstitious teaching of the nuns
in parochial schools. Now I would explain, if I got the chance,
that the hypothetical nuns, in my case, are blameless; that I was
never contaminated by a Catholic education. But why bother?
The fact remains that I *am* pre–World War II. (And so, alas, is
the Pope. Why they ever elected a man over twenty-five, I'll
never understand.)

Now no one is going to believe this (certainly, not young semi-
narians) but when I entered the Church, back in the Ice Age,

I was firmly presented with a missal. (Repeat, a missal. Not a rosary or a scapular or a box of matches for lighting candles during Mass.) And, since I *could* read the English alongside the Latin, I had the idiotic notion that I *was* participating.

Question: Who x-rays the minds and hearts of the worshippers and determines their participation rating? For all of that, how do I—down in the trenches—know that the priest is fully awake and participating?

Next, I was introduced to Dorothy Day, who had a faint glimmering about being your brother's keeper, and the Catholic Worker movement. Next, to Caryll Houselander whose whole school of spirituality was based on seeing the "unconscious Christ" in even our most unlikely neighbor. Next, to the Baroness de Hueck, with her Friendship House movement, and Father LaFarge: all knocking themselves out for the Negro. Twenty years ago, Negroes *were* sitting around my living room; I even found myself giving lectures on race prejudice down in Alabama. (Nowadays, you must quickly produce your Civil Rights credentials—and get clearance—or you're in for another sermon, willy-nilly.) And, quite naturally, I found myself in inter-faith groups—promoting understanding and friendship—and wound up with a dialogue, in book form, with a Unitarian. Which is about as far out as you can get.

So, forgive me if I now mutter "big deal" as the Jew is officially welcomed back to the human race, race prejudice is condemned, religious freedom is proclaimed. These are NEW teachings of the Church? I just never believed, nor was taught, otherwise. Really, if the Church now announces that it frowns on infant sacrifices or burying widows with their husbands, I shall run for cover.

I also mutter a faint "big deal" when it comes to lay commentators. Not only was my husband doing this five years ago, but this past year (that we spent in Europe) I discovered they have small boys of eleven or twelve handling the job. So, I wouldn't call it exactly a giant step forward for our American laymen or too weighty a responsibility. Ditto the laymen who are nabbed at the door and asked to walk up to the altar at the offertory. It's a nice liturgical gesture but does it mean so very much? (And can't they give the poor priest, sitting there like a wax dummy, *something* to do? Polish the candlesticks or something?)

What I think would be nice—would make for *real* participation for everyone—would be for a little adult discussion from the pulpit as to what in heck is going on in the doctrinal world. We *know* that the altar has been turned around—we can see it—but if the world of theology has not only been turned around but stood on its head, clue us in. And if our children in the Catholic high schools and colleges are being taught this new theology, *and they are*, why must the parents—like the betrayed wife—be the last to find it out?

Might it not be possible for the parish priest to turn off the love and brotherhood bit, for perhaps just one Sunday per month, and lay down some theological guidelines for us? Now if the priest himself, at this point, is as theologically confused as the laity, let him step bravely forth and confess it: it would create an enormous bond of love and brotherhood between them. And let him speak honestly. None of this "You understand, of course, that the Church has never officially taught such-and-such as doctrine." I understand no such thing. If a doctrine is taught in convert instruction, repeatedly preached from the pulpit, appears in all books with imprimaturs not to mention the Catholic press at large, well, now, wouldn't you say it *has* been taught? Maybe it's dead wrong, or non-dogmatic matter has been presented dogmatically, but let's have no doubletalk. "Taught" is the correct word.

(Oh boy, is this ever fun! I can't be accused of heresy—too stupid—and I can't be burned at the stake—religious persecutions went out last week—and the worst that can happen, and no doubt will happen, will be a rejection slip by return mail. These are the golden years. . . .)

Underneath the surface, people are disturbed. Mightily disturbed. They sing their hymns, with great good will, and then return to the firing line: having their children tell them that Mass is no longer obligatory (it's on the love basis now); that the no-meat-on-Friday is legalistic and old hat; that they must start from scratch in their faith (since the existence of God cannot be proved) and have their own "encounter with Christ." And, oh yes, that it's now perfectly okay to attend Protestant Sunday services and worship alongside their friends.

If all this be true, fine, it shaketh not my faith; but how do you find out? I hear nothing from the pulpit, nothing in the diocesan paper.

Perhaps this new (about 400 years new!) approach is marvelous—I wouldn't know—but if I were to start a schism, I think my rallying call would be this: "Clue us old-timers in. We may be ready for the glue factory but our faith is important to us, too. It just isn't cricket: all this tearing down, behind our backs, and giving us no briefing on the building up."

My schism might also call for a New Testament translation that *hasn't* been reduced (for the alleged benefit of the "common man") to the pedestrian prose of a government pamphlet on agriculture. I mean, if the new generation doesn't know the meaning of, say, "shepherd" or "sheep," let them *reach*. Let them wrestle, and figure out for themselves, that a "whited sepulchre" is a "whitewashed tomb" for they still gotta figure out, you know, what the imagery stands for. It seems to me that the world's greatest leaders, such as Churchill, for one, reached through to the common man, and even inspired him, by using a pretty high level of speech.

Oh, and while we're about it, how about a new set of labels? "Individualist" is a mighty nasty word, and one that I'm stuck with till my dying day, but how do I beat the rap? How do you write, and give talks, and answer letters from readers *except* as an individual? Even nastier, of course, is the word "arch conservative," which is what Bishop Pike flings at those who cling to the Trinity. I ask, wouldn't it be refreshing to introduce a whole new batch of labels and start over? Back in my Camp Fire days, we had titles like "wood gatherer," "fire maker," "trail maker," "torch bearer" and, in the swimming area, we were labeled either "pollywog" or "frog" or "fish."

Well, it's just an idea—I toss it in for free—and anyone who wants to start off by calling me an "arch pollywog," okay. I must tell you, though, that I once was labeled a Catholic humorist. I used to say, in dead earnest: "What if I, as convert, accept this bill of goods and then the Church changes its mind?" Everybody used to howl their heads off; they thought I was a riot. It gained me quite a reputation as a stand-up comedian, and any number of dinner invitations.

18. *CARTOONS by Charles Healy**

* From December 1967, February–March 1968, April–May 1968, June–July 1968, August–September 1968, October–November 1969, February–March 1968 issues of *The Critic*.

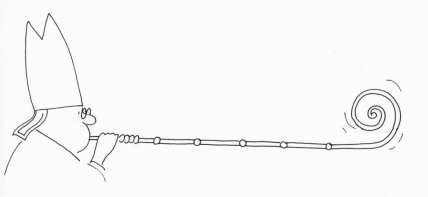

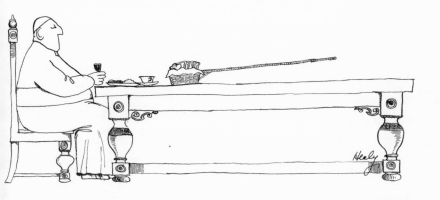

"Hello. This is Sister Elizabeth Michael at St. John's. Could you pick me up Saturday morning at 9:00 o'clock and take me to the A&P to do the shopping? This is a recording."

19. *GALILEO RE-TRIED**

by Joel Wells

PADUA, AUGUST 1—In one of the most closely watched trials of the past week, Italian scientist Galileo Galilei today rejected the Catholic Church's attempt to reinstate in its good graces his theory (now widely held by Protestants and Jews) that the earth revolves around the sun.

"If the Church said I was wrong, then I was wrong," said the four-hundred-four-year-old mathematician (who is credited with formulating the laws of the pendulum, the free fall of objects and the flight of projectiles). "I abjured and recanted the theory of the earth's motion in 1633 and I see no reason to change my stand now," he said at a press conference following today's trial by a special blue ribbon panel of inquisitors which met in closed session here in the private chambers of the Grand Inquisitor.

"That theory was thought up by Copernicus in the first place," the gray-bearded thinker said, "and for a while I thought he was on the right track. Where I went wrong was in teaching it as an established fact when I never had any mathematical proof. And I did so in the face of scripture, tradition and against the Holy Father's express wish that I cease and desist. I don't see what all

* From the August 1, 1968, issue of *Overview*.

151

the fuss is about. People still speak of sunrise and sunset—what's the difference which motion causes it."

Said a spokesman for the inquisition: "We are most distressed by Dr. Galileo's stand. It is seldom that the Church gives a man a second chance. We thought he would be delighted at this opportunity to undo the harm he did by so wrongfully teaching the truth before the Church had a chance to discover it for itself. But Dr. Galileo has proved to be a most obdurate son of the Church. It's a shame. In the old days we would have had no difficulty making him see things our way."

Xavier Rynne, a correspondent for the *New Yorker* magazine, who claims to have gained access to today's hearing, reports that Galileo denounced the members of the court as "turncoats and underminers of the faith." "He gave them holy hell," said Rynne, who is widely known for his colorful reporting of the Second Vatican Council. "He told them that they were the ones who should be brought to trial for questioning a decision of the Church at a time when papal authority and the Magisterium were already under attack by 'pinkos, freethinkers, theological perverts and the minions of scientific materialism.' "

According to Rynne, Galileo refused to hear a special plea from Cardinal Koenig or to meet with a delegation of Catholic Nobel Prize–winners who had flown here secretly to honor the scientist at a banquet following the trial.

In Uppsala, news of the trial was received with mixed emotions. Cries of "Three cheers for Galileo!" and "Revisionist dog!" swept back and forth across the floor of the assembly and several fist fights were reported. A highly placed spokesman for the World Council of Churches, who requested that he not be identified, said, "I could have told them not to bother—once a Catholic, always a Catholic. If anyone still thinks that ecumenism is more than a paper tiger, this should convince him."

In Rome, observers close to the Vatican told of a brief flurry of unusual activity around the papal chambers and noted that all papal audiences had been cancelled for the balance of the week.

An editor of *L'Osservatore Romano*, official organ of the Vatican, declined to comment pending knowledge of what his opinion was going to be.

Meanwhile, from Paris, word came that General de Gaulle, who had been following reports of the trial by transistor radio from atop the Sorbonne, had commented: "The truth has been served; the sun, as always, continues to revolve about me."

20. DEAR MOTHER*

by Rev. Joseph E. Kokjohn

St. Paul's Rectory
Greenley
February 9

DEAR MOTHER,

I presume the Bishop used good judgment, after all, in ordaining earlier than usual—at least as far as I'm concerned. The First Mass and everything went off very well, don't you think? Of course, you deserve full credit for that.

Speaking of work, I can see that there is plenty to be done here. As you know, the pastor is confined to the hospital. I checked in with him yesterday when I arrived and found him very agreeable. He has been ordained forty-seven years, but more or less retired for the past four or five. We didn't have much to talk about, of course, but I trust we shall have, once things begin to crystalize. I understand the assistant who preceded me spent most of his time reading.

The buildings are . . . well . . . decent: a big church (pseudo-Gothic) for this size parish, an eight-room school, and an over-sized gymnasium. I haven't been in the convent as yet, but it

* From the December 1964–January 1965 issue of *The Critic*.

appears to be in need of serious repairs. The rectory is spacious but not in harmony with the other buildings—in the style like Aunt Margaret's place. I have two rooms and a bath furnished with odds and ends someone must have picked up at the Salvation Army. The pastor's suite is furnished with a bit more taste, but not much. You would be horrified at the housekeeper's room: undergarments hanging over every piece of furniture and cardboard boxes protruding in every direction. It is in total keeping with her personality; she wears a hearing-aid and looks like she spent too much time under the hair-dryer.

After I have everything arranged and have sort of established myself, I think I shall find it satisfactory. Several parishioners introduced themselves after Mass this morning. One elderly woman said I looked so young that she feared she would never be able to approach me in the confessional. Poor soul—she was at the vigil light stand before, after, and possibly during Mass—a regular pyromaniac. But, as I said, things will be satisfactory, especially when I have my own car. One of the dealers belongs to the parish and will probably call on me when he discovers I am a likely prospect.

Well, Mother, I must visit the school now.

> *à la française, Dieu avec nous*
> Father Donald McKeever

P.S. My first baptism is scheduled for Sunday afternoon.

Sunday, 4:00

Dear Donald,

You write the most beautiful and interesting letters, and all afternoon I couldn't think of anything but your first baptism. How lovely! Boy or girl? I just wish I could've been there with you.

I think so too, about the Bishop ordaining early. What more could they have taught you by waiting till spring. Too bad the pastor has to be in the hospital that way, but I'm sure you can handle everything all right. Your father would be so proud of you if he was still with us, wouldn't he?

I had my hair fixed Tuesday afternoon. Aunt Margaret thinks it looks a little youngish for me, but I told her I'm not ready for the grave. And I want you to look out after your appearances. Priests are in the public eye. That new suit you got for ordination is swell and fits you across the shoulders—makes you look so solid. And your new coat is swell too.

I can hardly wait till you get that new car and I'm sure that dealer will stop by when he finds you're without one. Don't go running after them, let them come to you.

People are still telling me how nice your First Mass was and what a nice voice you have for singing. It really was lovely and we had such nice weather for it. Hope it keeps up.

Is the housekeeper really as bad as you say? Hope she keeps *your* room better than she does her own. I suppose housekeepers can be problems just like everyone else. Well we all have our little crosses. Now, if you want anything, just let me know and I'll get it.

Love,
Mother

St. Paul's Rectory
Greenley
February 15

Dear Mother,

What a furious week-end I had: I offered the two early Masses and preached at both of them—the Church Fathers' concept of mental prayer. Father Savage from St. Gregory's College had the other two. Perhaps you remember he taught me English, the one who spent so much time on Chaucer and Burns, the eighteenth century poet. There's a great deal to be desired in his preaching too, from what I heard of his sermon—something vague on the virtues. For me, at least, he was extremely disappointing. In the afternoon I had that baptism, a *boy* who slept almost completely through the administration of the sacrament.

After that I walked over to the hospital and spent two hours with Father Travis. Every time I offered a suggestion he artfully changed the subject. I'm beginning to think that the former assistant *had* to do a lot of reading, just to appease the pastor. He intimated that I should spend a maximum of only forty-five minutes a day in the school. On the other hand, he does want me to spend more time visiting in the hospital.

From the way he talks, I surmise that he places a great deal of trust and confidence in the housekeeper, certainly more than I ever would. I believe that she's completely illiterate. She is even in possession of the keys to his car.

At the moment I have three persons under instruction, which of all my duities I relish most. Although they are quite slow, they appear to be eager, which is a compensation. Undoubtedly I shall have to take much more time with them than I had anticipated.

As I told you, the convent is in need of repairs. I have hired a reprobate, who came with a hard-luck story, to do some painting in the convent's drab dining room.

Sincerely,
Father Donald McKeever

P.S. The car dealer still has not come around, so I think I'll get the keys to Father Travis's car and use it until I have my own. Thus far the housekeeper has not been very particular about my laundry, but I have persuaded her to answer the door and telephone.

Sunday, 4:00

Dear Father Donald,

Aunt Margaret thinks your letters are interesting too. She said she remembers back when Father Travis was an assistant at the

Cathedral and wants to know if he's still so good looking. That must have been forty or forty-five years ago. Maybe you can drop her a line when you find time.

I had my hair done over because it did look a little youngish and I don't want to look like I'm trying to pass for a high school girl. Speaking of school, how is your teaching going? I think it's swell you have the opportunity to teach and get all that experience around the hospital. Father Travis sounds like he has a lot of good sense. There are some pastors I wouldn't like you to be stationed with, so I hope you'll be there for a long time. And three instructions! The people must like you.

Remember when I told you about your clothes and if the housekeeper doesn't take care of them, just send them home and I'll do them for you. Now, don't hesitate.

The weatherman says we can look for some snow for the next several weeks, so maybe you're lucky you don't have your new car yet. I don't see anything wrong in using the pastor's as long as he's in the hospital and can't use it, but be careful and find out whether or not he has insurance.

I know you're very busy trying to run the parish all alone but write whenever you can. I'll send you some home-made cookies this week.

Love,
Mother

St. Paul's Rectory
Greenley
February 24

Dear Mother,

I had another strenuous week and consequently my correspondence is a few days late. Incidentally, please don't show my letters to Aunt Margaret. You can never tell whom she might talk to and what she might say. Those instructions, for example, were started by the previous assistant. Thus far I have not had time to contact any new prospects. Perhaps I'll have more time since Father Travis has suggested that I discontinue teaching catechism. I hope my absence from the classroom will not interfere with the soccer team I am organizing.

I have had several pleasant visits with him since I last wrote. As old as he is, he is very admirable and, as you said, has a lot of common sense. He has offered to buy me some books, but I would prefer some new records, or even new drapes.

When I received your last letter, I informed Alice, the house-keeper, that you would take care of my laundry. She pretended not to hear, but the next day she took almost every stitch I have and washed and ironed it. Undoubtedly she knows where I stand now on the laundry issue. My new mission is attempting to keep the thermostat lower.

Thus far the car dealer has kept his distance, but I'll persevere as long as he will. Yesterday I discovered the keys to Father Travis's car and drove up to see Father Foley at Stillwater. Oh, dear, what an abominable parish! Father Travis's car is practically new with only a little more than a thousand miles on it.

I have made lunch of the cookies several days, twice when having *carrot* and *celery* soup! She makes Lent a very rigorous affair. And she must have been diagnosed as anemic, for all the liver and onions she serves. But I think she will gradually come around.

Pax tecum!
Father Donald McKeever
Assistant Pastor

P.S. We had a mellow cocoa paint for the dining room in the convent, but the sisters thought it a bit dreary after one wall was painted. We have changed to a seafoam green. We're going to surprise Father with it when he is released from the hospital.

Sunday, 7:00

Dear Father Donald,

I went to a show this afternoon with Aunt Margaret and then we ate out. The show was utterly disgusting, but Aunt Margaret insists on going every so often. We had a swell dinner at the Carlton Hotel, and she insisted on paying for it. I had some of your favorite *au gratin* potatoes.

Teaching can be a real strain and I suppose that's why Father Travis wants you to take it a little easy. That seminary was not easy going and he probably realizes that you're exhausted. Just take it easy for a while. You deserve it, after all.

I'm so glad the housekeeper (the name Alice sounds like it fits her perfectly) is looking after your clothes better. Priests are in the public eye. Aunt Margaret is always asking about you and wants to know if you need anything. You have a birthday coming up and she has plenty to spend, so let me know.

Did you get much snow? We had three inches yesterday and the weatherman says we are due for more. I'm so glad you can get out and take a drive now, but don't have any accidents.

I'm going to send you some of Aunt Margaret's homemade sauerkraut with caraway seed. I hope the post office is careful with it. Tell Alice all she has to do is cook it slowly for about an hour and forty-five minutes.

Love,
Mother

Sunday, 4:00

Dear Father Donald,

I didn't hear from you this week. I hope you haven't been sick. If you can't find time to write, just call me—and reverse the charges if you want to. I didn't call because I thought it might upset you. Long distance can be expensive.

We didn't get that big snow the weatherman predicted, but I

heard that you got the tail-end of it. Won't you be glad when this winter is over? I think it has been one of the worst. It hasn't agreed with Aunt Margaret either, and the doctor told her to stay in until the weather is better.

Did you get the sauerkraut all right? I was very careful about packing it. Let me know whether Alice ate any of it, or is she the type who won't eat anything but her own cooking? I thought that was cute about her being anemic. (Did I spell that right?) Don't let her lord it over you just because she has seniority.

I'll be expecting a letter.

Love,
Mother

P.S. I like my job at Penney's all right—meeting people and everything. Some of the young clerks are sort of seedy, but I think I'll be able to adjust after a few days.

St. Paul's Rectory
Greenley
March 9, Feast of St.
Frances of Rome

Dear Mother,

The sauerkraut arrived in excellent condition. After unwrapping it, I took it to the kitchen and gave Alice the instructions for preparing it. But it slipped out of her hands and broke right there on the kitchen floor. I am quite certain that it was accidental, as she seemed so very apologetic.

My relations with her have been improving gradually, but she still insists on keeping the thermostat set very high. (By placing a piece of tape on it, however, I think I can remedy the situation.) She still has not been persuaded into realizing that I have a right to Father Travis's car. That is one point she is adamant upon.

In general the parochial tasks are running quite smoothly. We now have the dining room, the music room, and pantry painted in the convent. Even Alice doesn't know about this project. She must have told Father that I am still going over to the school and teaching regularly, as he asked about it. But he just doesn't realize the importance of having competent religion teachers for those youngsters. Then, too, I attempt to spend more time with the boys after school practicing soccer. Merely teaching them the fundamentals of protecting themselves keeps one busy.

One of the persons under instruction has not been keeping his appointments, but I believe that I have another prospect to replace him. I have been spending many hours in organizing a Study Club. As you can surmise, Greenley leaves a great deal to be desired culturally. For that reason I am making it civic rather than parochial. Four members attended the first meeting, including a Methodist minister of extraordinary talent. The Church can stand a little prestige in a place of this type.

Father Travis is much better and has asked me to thank you for the get-well card. He was sitting up today. With his white hair, florid face, bathrobe and gold-knobbed walking stick he was quite the picture of conservatism.

Pax tecum!
Father Donald McKeever
Assistant Pastor

2830 Beacher Avenue
Kingston
March 12, Fourth Sunday
of Lent

Dear Alice,

Let me introduce myself. I am Father McKeever's mother, and a worried mother, perhaps without reason. I know you can't look out after him like his own mother can, but he isn't powerfully strong physically and needs a little care.

For eight years I prayed that college and seminary would not be too much for him, with all its rules and stuff. Now he is ordained and will make a swell priest if he doesn't have to worry about his constitution. He sweats a lot, and in the food line he likes sweets (chocolate cake, his favorite), can't stand pork and liver, likes those *au gratin* potatoes and fresh peas, but not too much for salads and that kind of stuff. I thought it might make cooking easier for you if you knew what to fix.

He's very particular about his clothes; I guess he takes after me. I appreciate the pains you must take with doing up his things, but he doesn't like too much starch in his shirts.

It took a lot of money to see him through college and seminary and First Mass (he'll probably show you the First Mass pictures), so he probably won't be able to buy a car right off. In a way I'm glad—sort of old-fashioned I guess. But he is a careful driver.

He's not the type to tell you what he likes and doesn't like, but I know you'll get along fine. He thinks you have a lovely parish. Please don't tell him I wrote. This can be just between the two of us.

Pax tecum!
Mrs. Clara McKeever

St. Paul's Rectory
Greenley
March 17, Feast of St. Patrick

Dear Mother,

I haven't heard from you this week, but I do trust you are feeling well. Father Travis has improved immensely in the last few days and we believe he should be coming home within a week or so.

I received the birthday box from you and Aunt Margaret. The smoking jacket is quite exquisite and will be put to good use. (Alice asked me what it was.) The record appears to have exceptional tonal quality, but I hope you did not deprive yourself for my sake.

We now have six members in the Study Club, in spite of a little opposition by two ministers in town. The Methodist minister is still coming; he shows a great deal of insight concerning ecumenical matters. The club had dinner here Tuesday night before our meeting. Not one of them had ever been inside the rectory, so I gave them a grand tour—except for Alice's room. Fortunately you sent the First Mass pictures in the birthday box; they all seemed very impressed with them.

Don't tell Aunt Margaret, but Father Travis can't remember her at all. I must be on my way to catechism now.

> *Dominus tecum!*
> Rev. Donald McKeever
> Assistant Pastor

P.S. The tape on the thermostat has been removed, so I have reverted temporarily to opening the windows upstairs. Father Foley has invited me to Forty Hours at Stillwater Sunday evening. *Dum vivimus, vivamus!*

Sunday, 4:00

Dear Father Donald,

I think the idea of organizing a Study Group is just swell. We don't have anything like that here in Kingston as far as I know. Maybe you can talk the pastor into getting one started.

When Father Travis gets home from the hospital, things should be a lot easier for you. I know you must be terribly busy with everything, but don't overwork yourself. Seminary was not as easy as some people think it is.

How has the food been? Better, I hope. I'm so glad you liked the smoking jacket. I picked it out. Maybe sometime this summer Aunt Margaret and me can come over and pick out some nice drapes for your room. I'm going to have some of the First Mass pictures enlarged, there are so many people who like them and have asked me for extras.

Well, Father Donald, I want to go over and see Aunt Margaret this evening, so bye for now. She gets so upset when I don't show up.

Love,
Mother

St. Paul's Rectory
Greenley
March 24, Feast of St. Gabriel

Dear Mother,

This has been a busy day, or rather, busy week again. I chaperoned the eighth grade to a movie this afternoon. It involved a bit of red tape but eventually all the problems were resolved. Fortunately I did not have to seek Father Travis's permission. I say fortunately since he is so insistent lately on a sort of hands-off policy where the school is concerned.

I forgot to mention that I now have my own set of keys to his car. Alice became almost vehement whenever I took them from their resting place in the kitchen cupboard. Having my own set will avoid unpleasantries.

The Study Group now has seven members, but several of them I can see are attending only for the social aspects involved. The Methodist minister is the most promising member and will make an excellent fishing companion come summer. We took a hike together yesterday morning and cooked our lunch amid the snow flurries and brisk wind. It was very invigorating and the talk most stimulating. However, I think he leans heavily toward rationalism.

The Forty Hours dinner at Stillwater was quite good for a rural parish. The missionary, on the contrary, was quite average, talking *down* to the people and full of inconsistencies. Father Savage continues to help out here on week-ends but does not make any effort to assist in counting the collection, helping with the baptisms, or improving his sermons. The evening I went to Stillwater I told Alice that I would eat out if she would help with counting the collection. She was completely taken in by the hoax.

I still have to make some preparations for my Lenten talk this evening—Pontius Pilot's Role in Redemption, so . . .

Sincerely,
Father Donald McKeever
Assistant Pastor

P.S. I have temporarily solved the hot-oven problem by moving a statue of St. Paul with a *vigil light* from the parlor to the corridor where the thermostat is situated.

Sunday, 4:00

Dear Father Donald,

How ingenious you are—the vigil light and thermostat, I mean. If she catches on to that, you can always try something else I suppose. That's so clever.

I quit my job at Penney's yesterday. I can get along with people all right as long as they keep their place. Here I am a grown woman and they tried to play practical jokes on me. I just can't take it like I could when I was younger. Aunt Margaret missed my visits too, so I think it's best all the way around that I quit.

We had a sermon this morning on rationalism and I wonder whether you should be going around with that minister. Father Travis might not like it either. You know these older people have their own ideas about things.

Aunt Margaret will be waiting for me if I don't hurry up. We're going to have a swell dinner at the Carlton again. Don't try to do too much. This is Holy Week and I know you'll be busy.

Love,
Mother

P.S. If Father Travis is still in the hospital next Sunday why don't you try to drive home and have supper with me and Aunt Margaret.

St. Paul's Rectory
Greenley
March 29, Monday of Holy Week

Dear Mother,

When I wrote last week that everything was going splendidly, I hadn't anticipated what the following days would bring. To hear Father Travis talk, one would think the multitudinous seas of adversity had burst their gates and ravaged Greenley. A few unpleasant incidents have occurred, but he has magnified everything out of all proportion.

Yesterday the Methodist minister used my name in his sermon and then *misquoted* me on what I had said about the gift of faith. It was not in the nature of an attack at all, but rather a very friendly and ecumenical gesture on his part. This got back to Father Travis along with the fact that the minister had dinner in the rectory the night our Study Club met here.

He also discovered, through one of the sisters, I'm sure, that we did some painting in the convent. This was to surprise him, but it rather infuriated him. He had plans for remodeling. In addition, one of the boys on the soccer team broke his leg, and the parents are holding the parish responsible for it. I understand that they made quite a scene of it in the hospital.

Only one joyful note: the car dealer has finally weakened under my perseverance. He has a demonstrator with hardly any miles on it and has made me a good offer. I didn't want to seem anxious, so I told him that *maybe* I would come around next week and discuss it with him. It will be extremely difficult to get around once Father Travis is released from the hospital.

Sincerely,
Father Donald McKeever
Assistant Pastor

P.S. Alice caught on and has returned St. Paul and vigil light to the parlor. Her meals haven't improved.

Wednesday, 7:00

Dear Father Donald,

Now don't you worry. Alice is on your side even if she pretends not to be. From what you tell me I think she will be able to persuade Father Travis that you were doing the best you could. Angels can do no better. Don't get all upset. Aunt Margaret sometimes gets disturbed too, but she gets over it all right. When people get older, you have to expect little blowups now and then. And after all, you were doing the best you could.

I know you'll feel better when you get some of Aunt Margaret's sauerkraut in your stomach. By the time you get this letter you should have it, since I mailed it yesterday to Alice personally.

Please try to come home Easter afternoon if you can. Aunt Margaret has promised to take us out to dinner if you come.

Love,
Mother

St. Paul's Rectory
Greenley
March 30, Friday of Holy Week

Dear Mother,

I went over and talked things over with Father Travis last night. We agreed that I should withdraw from the Study Club and disband the soccer team. Perhaps later I can renew my interest in them.

After that it was quite late but, nevertheless, I stopped by and told the Methodist minister what we had decided. I distinctly remember leaving the garage door open so I wouldn't disturb Alice when I came in. Her room is right next to the garage. When I returned, however, it was closed. Of course I wasn't anticipating the door would be closed, and there must have been a patch of ice right in front of the garage, because I went right through the door—up to the windshield. The insurance will cover most of the expenses, Alice told me, but it is metaphysically impossible to have the car repaired before Father Travis returns Sunday. Had it been planned, the timing could not have been less propitious. Alice, of all things, seems a bit amused at my consternation.

I trust you and Aunt Margaret will have a happy Easter without me.

Deus misereatur!
Father Donald McKeever

21. *ROUND TRIP**

by Charles Healy

ON THE WALL of the stairwell, pictures of Saints gradually
ascended to the second floor or, as the nuns liked to think, to
heaven. (Coming *down* the stairs the analogy was suspended.)
Sister Rita and Sister Superior stood at the foot of the stairs speaking in low voices.

"I hope you don't mind going, Sister," Sister Superior said.
"We could order the books by mail, but she loves to get out once
in a while."

"That's all right, Sister. I really don't mind."

Sister Raphael appeared at the top of the stairs carrying an
umbrella and an empty, wrinkled shopping bag. When she saw
the Superior she stepped back out of sight, but it was too late.

"I don't think that's a good idea, Sister," Sister Superior called
up the stairs.

Sister Raphael poked her head over the banister. "What isn't,
Sister?"

"The white shoes."

"White shoes?"

"Yes, Sister." The Superior nodded at what looked like a white

* From the April–May 1966 issue of *The Critic*.

mouse peeking around the base of the banister post. When Sister
Raphael looked down, it darted out of sight.

"They're very cool," Sister Raphael said absently, looking at
the spot where her foot had been. Then, looking down at the two
nuns, "They have tiny air holes, you know." But there wasn't any
fight in her voice and after a few moments she disappeared.

"She's always trying to slip out with those on," Sister Superior
said. "They're from the time she was stationed at the hospital,
St. Clair's. She doesn't realize they look all right with the white
habit, but they look silly with the black."

Sister Rita, who didn't look that old, went, "Tsk, tsk."

"I told her if she likes them so much she should dye them
black, but of course she won't. She says the dye would block
the air holes so her feet can't breathe."

"Isn't that something," Sister Rita said, shaking her head. "The
poor thing."

Upon hearing Sister Raphael's cell door open and close, the
Superior gave a little wave and moved away. When Raphael came
down, she and Rita made a brief visit to the chapel, then went
to the front door. Rita removed the chain and the bolt while
Raphael, impeded as much by her umbrella, shopping bag and
Little Office as by old age, was still fumbling with the key. Outside, they walked to Mr. Ryan's car which was double-parked
in front of the convent.

Whenever he was angry or upset, Mr. Ryan's lower jaw stuck
out like a car ash tray. Now, waiting for the nuns, his jaw was
out far enough to accommodate a fat stogie. Several months
before, he had picked up Sister Raphael and a younger nun
uptown and given them a ride back to the convent. He had
always thought that nuns were only allowed out to visit the sick
or attend funerals, so he hadn't foreseen any danger in inviting
them to call on him any time they needed a ride. And that's when
the dam burst. He couldn't begin to estimate how many miles he
had logged since then with a carful of nuns. Especially that old
one. She seemed to spend more time out than in. (And Mr. Ryan

suspected that all her trips weren't on the up and up. Once she had called him and, in a whisper, was telling him when to pick her up. Suddenly she said, "I can't talk now," and hung up.) She seemed to Mr. Ryan like a child who would run until she dropped, and he imagined one of the nuns tucking her in ("Night-night!") while she, wearing a bonnet like one of those plastic dish covers, looked up bright-eyed from her pillow, ready to leap out of bed the moment the other nun left the room.

She was a sketch all right. Her and those beads. If he jumped a light or cut in too soon, she'd pipe up, "Shall we say a rosary, Sisters, for a safe trip?"

They'd cost him money, too. Mr. Ryan had an appliance store, and he figured it would be good for business if word got around that he had given the nuns a couple of items at cost. Well, before they were through they'd gotten a refrigerator, a freezer and half a dozen window fans. Mr. Ryan looked ruefully up at the convent. With two of his largest fans slowly spinning in the parlor windows, it looked like a Victorian houseboat run aground. When he remembered how much he would have made on them retail, he looked away, so he didn't see the two nuns come out.

"Good afternoon, Mr. Ryan," Sister Rita said as she opened the back door. Mr. Ryan started to get out, but Sister Rita told him to stay put, because he was double-parked (was that a crack?) and would have to step into traffic. "And we don't want to lose our favorite chauffeur." Ordinarily Mr. Ryan would have gotten out anyway, but the pants he had on were so small that the zipper showed in a toothy V just below his shirt. He closed his door and sat back.

Rita got in first so that Raphael would not have to climb to the far side of the car, but when she sat down she saw that the older nun was already settled in the front seat and rolling down the window. Rita moved back to the other side, closed the door, and sat down with a sigh. In front of her, Raphael's head, a small, smooth melon under the black veil, barely showed above the seat. Rita wondered idly if Raphael could even see out the window.

"Ground chuck, two pounds eighty-nine cents," Raphael called out, reading a sign in an A&P window. "We'll have to tell Sister Irma about that, Sister."

"Yes, Sister," Sister Rita answered, but the car and Sister Raphael had already gone on to something else.

"Donleavey's Bar and Grill. Tables for Ladies." Raphael turned her head so that Rita could see her profile through the side of her veil. With all signs of femininity gone from her face, she might have been a priest hearing confessions. "I wonder if that could be the Donleavey boy in your class, Sister."

Rita hadn't known before that Danny Donleavey's father owned a tavern. But she had once asked the children to bring in dust cloths for washing down the blackboard and Danny had brought in a blue-checked tablecloth. The tablecloth was like new so that rather than tear it up for dust rags, Rita had used it on the May altar—a table at the rear of the classroom which held a statue of the Blessed Mother and was decked with flowers for the month of May. The tablecloth was just like those Rita saw on the Tables for Ladies, and she bit her lip as she remembered her remark as she had smoothed the cloth around the statue. "Isn't that lovely, children? And it's blue, Our Lady's color."

Our Lady's color! "I don't know, Sister," she said.

While Raphael continued to read signs aloud, Rita found herself frowning at the statues of St. Patrick and St. Francis on the dashboard. She had disapproved of them from the first time she saw one. ("It's St. Christopher," Raphael had said, attaching the statue to the radiator at a hazardous angle. "He has a magnetic bottom.") Rita preferred her Saints in a setting of candlelight and stained glass—not windshield wipers and oncoming traffic—but she kept her opinion to herself when she learned that the Bishop not only approved of them but was something of a collector. Anxious not to offend any nationality, His Excellency had a standing order for one of every statue produced. The dashboard of his Fleetwood now looked like a mob scene from a biblical movie, and Father O'Bannion insisted that he had spotted Charlton Heston in the crowd.

They were passing a block which was completely torn down for redevelopment, so Raphael turned her attention to Mr. Ryan.

"How's that special intention coming?"

"Pardon, Sister."

"That special intention you wanted me to pray for."

"Oh, that. Fine, Sister."

Rita turned quickly to the window. The test of her Christian charity was never greater than when Raphael got on the subject of special intentions, and she was afraid that if Mr. Ryan caught her eye in the rear-view mirror (he seemed to be trying to make contact every time Raphael said something), she would go smiling over to the enemy.

Wherever she went, Raphael distributed prayers like tips. If a waitress or sales clerk was particularly attentive, she would ask if they had a special intention they'd like her to pray for. Of course it's common practice for people to ask nuns to pray for them. But it's also common practice for nuns simply to make the intention to add that person to their prayers and let it go at that. (Rita, wary of freeloaders, always stipulated that the requestor be praying too.) But not Raphael. Once someone agreed that, yes, there was something she might pray for, Raphael wondered aloud if they didn't want to tell her exactly what the intention was. Her tone insinuated that this information would help her to pipe the request through the proper channels—St. Christopher for the safe return of a loved one, St. Jude for hopeless cases ("Of course, I'm not making any promises").

Rita was happy to see that most people, claiming that special intentions, like wishes, must be kept secret to come true, denied Raphael this information. (One sad exception was a book store clerk who, under pressure from Raphael, admitted that his marriage was in trouble because he was impotent. Fortunately, Raphael thought impotence had something to do with being re-tarded and came away saying, "He seemed intelligent enough to

me.") Rita was certain that many of these people didn't really
have any intention in mind and were just being nice to Raphael.
And, although she knew there must be a kind of celestial clearing
house to reroute such pointless prayers to the Poor Souls in Purga-
tory, it depressed her to think how many of Raphael's prayers,
like the dime given for coffee and spent on drink, were sent aloft
for fictitious causes. She imagined a heavenly clerk frowning over
a scrap of parchment and calling out, "Anybody got anything on
a Mrs. Dixon, runs a religious supply store?"

And another thing: Raphael, in a misguided sense of humility,
seemed to have put an exact limit on just how many intentions
she could take on before her effectiveness as an intermediary
suffered. Thus, someone who casually asked her to pray for a sick
aunt would be checked periodically to see if the aunt had died
or mended sufficiently to be taken off Raphael's danger list.

"Did you get it?" Raphael asked Mr. Ryan.

"Get what, Sister?"

"What I was praying for."

"Oh. Yes. Yes, I did."

"Good." Raphael reached into her pocket, brought out a small
notebook, then took a lead pencil out of a holster on her belt.
She opened the notebook and started to make a mark. Then she
paused and looked at Mr. Ryan.

"Is there anything else?"

"Pardon, Sister."

"Do you want me to pray for something else?"

"No, thank you, Sister."

"No special intentions?"

"I don't think so, Sister."

Raphael nodded, made a mark in the book (presumably through
Mr. Ryan's name), then wrote something directly under it.

My Lord! Sister Rita thought, she has a waiting list.

"Tom and Jerry's Newsstand," Rapahel called out as she put
the pad and pencil away. "That's where Monsignor gets his
papers." Then, looking at Mr. Ryan, she added, "They deliver."

Rita wasn't sure whether this was added to assure Mr. Ryan that Monsignor had more important things to do than to go out for the papers or to feed the rumor that Monsignor hadn't been out of the rectory in ten years.

The car crawled to a traffic light. As the light turned orange, Mr. Ryan threw the car into second gear and cut left across the intersection before the oncoming traffic knew what hit it. A teen-age boy in a two-tone Ford tried to beat him out but, with the extra weight of a spotlight, fog lights and a plump girl who seemed absorbed with something going on inside his ear, he had to settle for leaning on his horn as he cut through Mr. Ryan's wake. Mr. Ryan, flushed with victory, saw that Sister Raphael had snatched at the beads hanging from her belt.

"Don't worry, Sister," Mr. Ryan said, waving a hand at the statues on the dashboard. "My little Saints take care of me."

"They're not watching the road either," Raphael snapped back.

Rita decided to change the subject before Raphael could utter any further blasphemies. She asked Mr. Ryan how his family was, although she knew that he was one of those people who took such questions literally: Mrs. Ryan was fine (apparently over that "woman trouble" he had told them about last time); Jeff's trick knee, an old football injury, was kicking up again; Marie was over her cold (but must have passed it on to him because he woke up this morning with the sniffles); and last but not least, little Annie was checking in St. Mary's next day to have her tonsils out.

By this time they had pulled up to the station and Raphael was on the edge of her seat, anxiously watching the train that had just pulled into the station. "We'll pray for a speedy recovery or happy death," she said as she stepped out of the car and headed for the station.

Rita hated to leave Mr. Ryan like that, but if she didn't hurry, Raphael, to her delight, would be on the train alone.

On the train, Rita put their tickets in the slot on the seat, but Raphael retrieved them.

"I want to see something," she said, putting the tickets into her pocket.

Raphael's habit, even as habits go, was large. The sleeves were very long (although they still managed to be half an inch shorter than the sleeves of her underwear), and the veil jutted far out around her face like a shadow box. Her face did not fill the coif so that when she turned her head the side jackknifed, revealing one of her very large ears. Raphael had been Rita's teacher in grammar school and in those days her coif had been as tight as a bathing cap, so Rita sometimes wondered whether this was a new habit or if, with advancing age, the old nun was shrinking up inside it. (She remembered with some guilt that she had made this observation a few nights ago in the community room and had gotten quite a laugh with the suggestion that, if Raphael lived long enough, she would disappear from sight altogether, her voice coming back to them as if from a well.) The overall effect was that Raphael lived in the habit rather than wore it.

When the conductor stopped and asked for their tickets, Rita nodded towards Sister Raphael, who was staring straight ahead.

"Tickets, please," the conductor repeated.

Raphael continued to stare ahead.

"Tickets, please."

Still nothing.

"Tickets, please."

The conductor seemed prepared to wait until doomsday, so Raphael played her trump card. She closed her eyes and began to move her lips, supposedly in prayer.

The conductor bent over and whispered very reverently, "Tickets, please."

Rita would have let the two of them fight it out if there was some way that she could give the other passengers the impression that she, Rita, by special permission from the Mother House, was traveling alone and, by some incredible coincidence, had landed next to another solitary nun who, though from the same order as Rita, was a total stranger to her. Failing that, Rita laid her hand on Raphael's arm. "*Sister!* the tickets." Raphael looked at her and nodded, then thrust one arm into her pocket up to the elbow. Dying hard, she thrashed about in her pocket for a while before producing the tickets and turning them over to the conductor.

As the conductor moved away, Raphael poked Rita with her elbow. "He must be a left-hander," she whispered. "But he looked as Irish as Paddy's pig." She shook her head wonderingly. "The last one's name was O'Brien, and he said we shouldn't even have *bought* tickets."

Rita, who didn't believe in trainmen giving out free rides on trains which were not their personal property, was glad the conductor had persevered. She opened her Little Office and had just started to read when Raphael jabbed her in the ribs again. "Maybe we'll get one of our own on the way back," she said in a whisper that could be heard halfway down the car.

In the Grand Central tunnel, the train inexplicably slowed and stopped several times, as if cows were crossing the tracks. Finally, the platform slid up to the train, and the two nuns, at Raphael's signal, stood up. Raphael took the lead and staggered down the aisle. She stopped a few inches from the door and stood staring at the glass as if waiting for her reflection to stand aside. When the conductor came through she followed him out of the car, and when he opened the door outside, she stood in the opening like a paratrooper, squinting into the wind. Rita, though the platform rushing by made her nervous, stood close behind Raphael in case she tried to step off before they reached the jump zone.

Sister Raphael seemed to know her way around Grand Central. She indicated some escalators, which had not been there the last time Sister Rita was in New York, and started towards them. Halfway there, her head jerked around and her hand shot up under her wimple. Rita caught her breath; at Raphael's age it could just as well be her heart as her watch. But it was her watch, which she checked against the huge clock across the station. As she replaced the watch in the small pocket on her breast, her wimple lifted, revealing the usual nun's jewelry: a scattering of common pins, one or two safety pins, one sewing needle flying its banner of black thread, and a Sacred Heart badge.

As soon as Raphael boarded the escalator she braced herself to get off. She stood facing square ahead, feet flat and elbows out so that the umbrella and shopping bag were clear. As she approached the top she went into a slight crouch and up on her toes, then was propelled forward, taking quick little steps to catch up with herself, like a vaudeville comedian pretending to have been pushed onstage. When they were on their way again, Raphael shook her head and said, "A person could get killed on one of those things," but it was clear from her expression that she considered it a beautiful way to go.

They went directly to a book store on Fifth Avenue and ordered some books for the school. When they came out Rita tried to steer Raphael back towards Grand Central. Instead, Raphael took Rita on a tour of five-and-ten-cent stores and in each one managed to become separated from the younger nun. At first, Rita thought these separations were accidental, but when she realized how long it took them to find each other, she began to suspect that she was the only one looking. Her suspicions were confirmed when, after they were reunited in the bowels of Lamston's hardware department, she saw that Raphael's shopping bag had begun to balloon.

Her first thought was that the old nun had been taking things unconsciously or naively, thinking everything was free for nuns. For a moment she considered turning her in, but the resulting scene which she imagined taking place in the manager's office dissuaded her: After explaining to the manager and the store detective that Raphael was like a child, really, and didn't mean any harm, the detective snarled, "We've heard that one before, lady." Then, sticking his cold cigar into his mouth to get it out of the way, he walked across the room and roughly raised Raphael's habit. There, in the folds of her petticoat, hung pots, pans, composition books, a pump action flit gun, a Japanese fan and other five-and-ten treasures. The scene seemed so real to Rita that, as they left the store, she caught herself listening to hear whether Raphael clanked when she walked. She didn't. She jingled.

So she had money. And God knows how many cadged taxi, train and bus rides it represented. Even if she hadn't caught a glimpse of the red cab of a toy truck, Rita would have known that the bag was filled with toys. And, even though she knew there was something in there earmarked for *her* nephew, she felt irritated. Why should Raphael have money to throw away while the rest of the nuns cut the signatures off Christmas cards received and sent them out the following year as their own? Why should Raphael have money to spend on things like the new umbrella she was carrying while the other nuns hung their patched underwear on the line inside pillowcases, a flapping chorus for Raphael's longjohns?

Apparently Raphael had done all the shopping she wanted to do because Rita now had little trouble getting her back to Grand Central and onto a train. Raphael grabbed the window seat and put the shopping bag between her legs. Rita offered to put the bag up in the rack.

"What shopping bag?" Raphael asked, snapping her legs together so that all that showed were the two looplike handles. They looked like grips placed there so that the old nun could be picked up. And Rita felt like doing just that—picking Raphael up and giving her a good shaking. Instead she sat and brooded over the humiliation the contents of the shopping bag promised for the next Visiting Sunday.

Visiting Days at the convent were hard on the children who were dragged along. There were no knickknacks to distract them (all the statues were symbolically out of reach), and their parents, intimidated perhaps by the murky oil paintings of heaven's citizens looking down their noses from every wall, never brought any toys along.

Rita did not blame the children for being restless and depressed. When she was first assigned to St. John's she felt the same way. The furniture was thick and angular and no two pieces seemed to be related, so that, looking around the room, her eye bumped along like a stick on a picket fence. What's more, the rooms were very high and so poorly lighted that it always seemed about to rain inside. Anyway, when the long afternoon began to tell on the children, and they seemed on the verge of climbing down from the chairs and running amuck in the wide, polished corridors, the nun whom they were visiting would bring out small gifts wrapped in tissue paper and tied with plain string.

These gifts were necessarily make-do affairs—odd items found around the convent, or gifts the nuns themselves had received. But they all had two things in common. First, they were religious. (Lay people, in despair over what you can possibly give to a nun, invariably settle on the one thing they had enough of.) Second, they were imperfect, for any articles in mint condition were displayed in a tall china closet, its dwarf legs buckling under the weight of statues, medals, missals and crucifixes. The closet was located in the main corridor, and the nuns were encouraged to steer visitors by it, mentioning in passing that the articles were for sale. (In doing this, Sister Rita always watched visitors' faces self-consciously for a flicker of recognition.)

Whatever enthusiasm was aroused by the appearance of the presents always fell off drastically when they were unwrapped, and in a few minutes the children would be squirming and whining again. At that point (had she been at the keyhole?) Raphael would poke her head in the door, make a quick head count, then disappear. A few minutes later she would return with an armful of gaily wrapped packages. There were yo-yos, tops, noise-makers, model airplanes and so on, and the children immediately forgot that, seconds before, they were crying to go bye-bye.

Rita frankly resented Raphael's interference in her visits. Her chances to ingratiate herself with her nephews were few (they came so seldom that a good part of the afternoon was spent getting them over their fear of the habit), so it was annoying to know that the high point of their visit was Sister Raphael's appearance. And if it wasn't for Rita's groundwork, the old nun would have been as welcome as the bogeyman, presents or no. Then, too, Rita knew that her sister and brother-in-law must wonder why she gave the children religious articles (and rejects at that) while old Sister what's-her-name went all out. Rita sometimes wondered if the reason they seldom brought the children was because George (who didn't go to Mass at all before Betty married him and now stayed awake only long enough to pick out something in the sermon to criticize) figured she was vocation hunting. In charity, of course, Rita couldn't explain the situation. So, as she sat grimly watching the children playing with Raphael's presents (and with Raphael herself, who got right down on the floor with them), she imagined the graces flowing into her soul like plasma. Somehow—and this worried her—it was a small consolation.

Rita interrupted her reflections when she became aware that the train was in a station and Raphael was twisting around in the seat, her face quite close to the window. A woman and three children on the platform seemed to be laughing and waving at Raphael so Rita leaned forward to see what was going on. She saw that Raphael was playing a child's game, pressing her face against the window until her nose and lips were bloodless blurbs. Before Rita could duck back, one of the children shouted, "There's another one!" Pressing back in her seat, Rita picked up where she had left off.

She remembered the time she went to see Sister Superior and told her that she was troubled by her attitude towards Sister Raphael. Sister Superior pooh-poohed Rita's idea that her feelings were sinful and admitted that on at least two occasions she herself had come within an inch of sending Raphael off to St. Agnes' —the rest home where the old nuns who are no longer useful in the classroom sit around listening to the dimming sound of clapping erasers and greeting their rare visitors with, "Where's your homework?"

"What happened?" Rita had asked, feeling better already.

The Superior told how she had found Raphael holding a pair

of luminous beads to the window as if to a crowd kneeling on the front lawn. When she asked what she was doing, Raphael had said, "Recharging them."

"And do you remember the time Sister Charlotte's relatives from California stopped to see her?" Sister Superior had gone on. "They were going to the World's Fair, and were to have started back again before Visiting Sunday, so I told her it was all right if they stopped. All her family lives so far away she only gets visitors about once a year anyway. Later, I dropped in St. Joseph's parlor to say hello, and Sister Raphael came in with a tray of tea and soda and cookies. And you remember Sister Charlotte's niece, the one about three?"

"Yes, she was very cute."

"Well, she looked up at the picture of the Bishop, the big one of him in his ermine cape and lace surplice, and she pointed at it and said, "Lady!"

Rita caught her breath as Sister Superior paused. She could tell from her expression there was more to come.

"Then," the Superior went on, "before anyone could correct the child, Sister Raphael said, "Yes, see the nice lady!"

After that, as if Sister Superior had passed the word, other nuns had volunteered stories about Raphael. Sister Matthew, for example, told of the time that her brother-in-law, a former pupil of Raphael's was about to go into the visitor's lavatory when Raphael came along with another nun. "I remember when you had to have my permission to go in there," she called out.

Sister Mary Clement told about the day she and Raphael were talking to Father Banner in the schoolyard. Just for something to say, Father pointed to a window on the second floor of the rectory and said, "That's my room."

"What are you telling us for?" Raphael said, cackling wildly.

And, of course, it was no secret that Mother General avoided meeting Raphael whenever possible, especially when lay people were around. It seems that, before her election, it was the custom for the nuns to keep their family names. However, when Sister

Hubbard became Mother Hubbard, she quickly pushed through an amendment (retroactive) whereby the nuns would take a Saint's name at Profession. (Those parents who objected to the fact that their daughters would not retain their family name could take some consolation in the knowledge that the change was inevitable: Sister Michael Peter, the former Mary McCree of the Waterbury McCrees, was a sure bet to succeed the present Mother General.) Raphael, however, had never been able to adjust to the change and still called all the oldtimers by their family names. So, at the annual bazaar held on the grounds of the novitiate, if you saw Mother General or Sister Thomas (nee Gladys Lipshitz) or Sister Estelle (nee Mary Twitty) ducking behind a bush or disappearing around a corner, you could be pretty sure that Raphael was pursuing in full call.

Although some of the nuns laughed when they told these stories, Rita knew that they were not simply amused by Sister Raphael's antics. The nuns knew too well that lay people tend to reason from the particular to the general ("Whatever you do, don't send your kid to a Catholic school. Why, I knew this nun once . . ."), so each felt a responsibility to every nun everywhere in her dealings with the outside world. Therefore it wasn't simply that Raphael didn't present the best face to the world, but, with her unique ability to get out of the convent on all kinds of spurious errands, she presented that face all too often.

When they got off the train, Raphael finally seemed to be tiring. But even as she walked slowly along she looked all about for some diversion. Rita, walking at her elbow, urging her along, felt as though she were carrying a split grocery bag, trying to get home before something fell out.

As they turned toward the corner where Mr. Ryan was to meet them, Raphael stopped and grabbed Rita by the arm.

"Sister! Look!" she said, pointing to a man lying on the sidewalk to the right of them. He was heavy, middle-aged and wore dark, rumpled clothing. His eyes were closed and his lips were moving as if he were trying to eat something without tasting it.

"He must be drunk," Rita said. She took a suggestive step toward the corner, but Raphael had already started over to the man. Rita wanted to keep on going, but knew she couldn't leave Raphael alone. And so she stood fretting, several yards away, a crowd of one giving him air.

Raphael crouched down next to the man, her umbrella slanting out from her side like a sword. She let go of her shopping bag and, after teetering for a few seconds, it toppled over, spilling some of its contents. A small car with a one-dimensional man at the wheel buzzed across the sidewalk toward Rita but ran down before it reached her. Raphael leaned close to the man.

"Can I help you?" she asked as calmly as if she were answering the door at the convent. The man moaned and his lips bubbled. Raphael leaned closer. "Are you a Catholic?" He moaned again, and his hands opened and closed at his sides. Rita shivered, hearing his nails scratch the pavement.

Suddenly the man started to breathe in great gasps, and his chest rose and fell violently. Raphael got down on her hands and knees and put her mouth close to his ear. "Make an Act of Contrition!" she shouted. "Tell God you're sorry!" The man's head and feet lifted at the same time, a fish curving on land. He gave another loud groan and at the height of it he seemed to shape it into a crude, "God!" Then he fell back and his head cracked against the pavement. A few moments later his closed fists relaxed.

When the ambulance arrived, the doctor started to examine the man while the driver went to the back of the ambulance to get an oxygen tank. When the driver walked over with the tank, the doctor told him to put it back and bring the stretcher.

As she watched them put the man on the stretcher, Rita wondered about the man's cry. It might have been an exclamation or a curse, but suppose it was a prayer? Since we are responsible for any sins we commit while drunk, because we are responsible for getting drunk in the first place, what about prayers said while we're drunk? It would seem that we're responsible for those too. So the man might have saved his soul without knowing it. It was an interesting question, but she put it out of her mind when she pictured the man staggering into heaven scratching his chest and mumbling, "Where the hell am I?"

The doctor started to cover the man's face with a blanket but, after glancing at the crowd, stopped it at his chest. As they lifted the stretcher into the ambulance, Raphael walked next to it smoothing the blanket.

"That's all right, Sister," the doctor said. "He's dead."

"Yes," Raphael said absently as she brushed away another wrinkle.

By the time they got back to the convent the nuns were already at supper, so Rita didn't see Sister Superior alone until the next morning.

"Did everything go all right yesterday?" Sister Superior asked after holding Rita in the corridor until the rest of the nuns had filed into chapel.

"Yes, Sister. Fine."

"I hope she wasn't too much trouble."

"I didn't mind, Sister. She enjoys it so."

"I know," Sister Superior said and placed her hand on Rita's arm. "I have to go to New York in a few weeks myself. I'll take you as my partner."

"Thank you, Sister. I'd like that."

They were interrupted by a clicking of beads.

"There you are," Raphael said, coming out of the chapel. "I thought you both died in your sleep."

She was about to say something else when a bell sounded, and they heard the nuns in chapel getting to their feet. Sister Raphael, whose voice always got away from her when she tried to whisper, said, "There's the bell!" Rita saw two boxers rushing to the center of the ring.

As slow as she was, Raphael was back in her seat before Rita and the Superior had even entered the chapel. It was almost as though they didn't want anyone to think they were with her.

22. *ISSUES THAT DIVIDE THE PANEL**

by Joel Wells

Dramatis Personae:

ROBERT ADROIT—Editor of *The National Catholic Revealer*, convener and moderator of the Panel.

REV. ANDREW M. SURVEY—Author, columnist and sociologist, Father Survey has many strings for his bow, or many bows for his string, depending on how you see it.

MISS JACQUELINE OVERWALL—Educator, soul-searcher, innovator and scene-stealer, Miss Overwall is so much in the news these days that people sometimes have difficulty knowing where else she is.

ARCHBISHOP DIRE—In the face of compelling pressures toward change, the affable and knowledgeable Archbishop has refused to settle for anything less than being a member of the hierarchy.

BRENT BOMBSHELL—The articulate editor of the recently founded magazine *Atrophy*, Mr. Bombshell is perhaps best known for his scheme to force time to run backwards or, failing that, at least to stand still.

DANIEL LIBERALHAND—Dynamic young scholar, journalist and

* From the April 15, 1967 issue of *Overview*.

author of a number of widely discussed books including the controversial *Dishonesty in the Diaspora*.

DR. GEORGE SCHOLASTIC—Years of experience in education, balanced wisdom, a reputation for coming through sticky situations without any gum on his soles—these are the qualities which Dr. Scholastic brings to the Panel.

Transcription:

MR. ADROIT: On the one hand, as you all know, or on the other hand, as you may not know, we're gathered here to discuss the most burning issues of the day . . .

FATHER SURVEY: Day? What day? Let's be specific. If we're going to begin with a lot of vague generalities, I'm going to take my statistics and go home.

MR. ADROIT: Well, then, this day—today . . .

ARCHBISHOP DIRE: I can't say that I care much for your use of that word "burning." It smacks of alarmism and sensationalism. Why disturb people unnecessarily?

MR. LIBERALHAND: Does the Archbishop mean to imply that people aren't already badly disturbed?

MISS OVERWALL: I sense a certain tension here—my feminine intuition tells me that this is not the way we should begin. Let's all think positively. Aside from Mr. Bombshell who is hopelessly out of it—though I don't for a moment deny his sincerity—I suspect that we could all find . . .

MR. BOMBSHELL: Well if you're in it, I'm just as glad to be out. But I think you've got it just backwards. At least I didn't run out on . . .

MR. ADROIT: Hold on! Let's not get personal. We're here to talk about issues and we'd better get on with it. I've drawn up a list of seven . . .

DR. SCHOLASTIC: I wonder if "issues" is precisely the term we should be using. I think in the public mind it's too much identified with politics. A more useful term might be realized if we examined the etymology of . . .

FATHER SURVEY: And how, pray tell, did you arrive at the number seven? What makes you think there aren't five, or fifty? I'd like to see your data.

MR. LIBERALHAND: And I resent your arbitrary decision against personalism. What is the people of God if it isn't an open personal interchange? I thought this sort of sterile angelism was buried with Pius IX.

MR. BOMBSHELL: I take it, then, that Mr. Liberalhand doesn't believe in angels? I suppose Michael, Gabriel and Raphael were really just ordinary people of God who managed to grow wings. And while you're correcting the magisterium would you mind explaining how you manage to bury a pure spirit in the first place?

MISS OVERWALL: Really, Mr. Bombshell, you have a streak of literalism in you a yard wide. Where's your flexibility, your feel for analogy? I really think you ought to move out of your defensive crouch and let the free interplay of ideas sweep over you. Why even the Archbishop knows that what Mr. Liberalhand meant was . . .

ARCHBISHOP DIRE: Please don't feel constrained to patronize me, Miss Overwall. I may not be blessed with your feminine instincts but I can take care of myself, I assure you. Now, if you'll all simply submit your questions in writing . . .

MR. ADROIT: No, no, no! This is all being recorded for transcription.

FATHER SURVEY: You weren't actually dreaming of publishing this verbal Dunkirk?

DR. SCHOLASTIC: I'd be remiss if I didn't say that I think the whole concept might profit from a careful rethinking.

MR. LIBERALHAND: I won't submit a thing in writing; it's an outdated medium of communication.

MISS OVERWALL: I intuit an impasse. If you'll excuse me, I've got to get my hair arranged for a network television appearance. But I want you to know how terribly open I feel toward you all.

MR. BOMBSHELL: I've got to see a man about a heresy.

MR. ADROIT: Oh well, I can probably get an editorial out of it, anyway.

FATHER SURVEY: I've got no objection to opinion as long as it's clearly labeled.

ARCHBISHOP DIRE: *Ite Panel Est!*

PEOPLE OF GOD: *Deo Gratias!*

23. ONE NUN AND THE MODERN WORLD*

Cartoons by Martin Murphy

"Now THAT I like!"

* From the April–May 1967 issue of *The Critic*.

"Sister! Sweetie! Baby!"

"I'm sure Sister will understand that Hollings is rather special."

*"Anything in our rule that says I can't give this
meathead a piece of my mind?"*

"*Quick! Grab a baseball and some bats! Here comes
a photographer.*"

"A penny for your thoughts, Sister."

"What's the matter, Sister, haven't you ever been whistled at before?"

"Let's go in and see if we can Christian them down a little."

"This will be our little secret, huh Timmy?"

*"If it wasn't for me you wouldn't be able to write
at all, Johnny Burke."*

24. *THE GOOD OLD DAYS**

by Rev. Joseph E. Kokjohn

WHAT AT ONE TIME was a venerable institution of security and comfort has recently been transformed into a "community" of experimentation, risk, and involvement, as if years of silent service, servility, and senility were worthy of nought. To be absolutely forthright, I cannot comprehend the irrevocable turmoil that has been foisted upon us since the demise of all the grand traditions which we fostered with unquestioned devotion. When I perceive this ineffable updating, avalanching on every side, I'm crushed with abashment and almost left speechless. What, I ask, has happened to the good old days?

Take my fourth-grade teacher for example, good old Sister Mary Boleslaus. She and her two sisters—Wratislaus and Kabbaslaus—entered the convent on the same day in order to work and pray for the souls of their aged and dying parents. Did they concern themselves with how their feeble parents would get along or who would care for them? No, they had a type of faith that we just don't see any longer in this shameful, secular world. They knew that life was a vale of tears, filled with vanity and bombast, and if God wanted to, He could stop the whole works with a jerk of

* From the April–May 1968 issue of *The Critic*.

His white beard. Today people no longer have that kind of faith —that glorious gift of passive acceptance. Today people go out and try to change things as if God were some kind of booby on the sixth day of creation.

Why, I can remember the day Sister Boleslaus' parents died from asphyxiation. Did she take a day or two off? I should say not. She stayed right there in the classroom and taught with renewed rigor. Can you imagine a nun doing that today? You can bet last Sunday's collection she wouldn't. Sister Boleslaus stayed in the classroom the entire day, even during recess, and we stayed right there with her and recited one rosary after another. When one of the boys wet on the floor, she bopped him a good one and made him clean up the mess with his jacket. Today they would send the brat to a psychiatrist for counseling. She was no Miss Congeniality, you understand, but she knew how to keep order—no fiddle-faddle with her.

Of course, much of the credit for our generation must also be given to people like old Monsignor McGuiness, my boyhood pastor of happy memory. Being human, he took a little too much to drink now and then, but there wasn't a grander person in town. Even some of the Germans liked him, and those Germans, with all their false superiority generated by the loss of two world wars, were not easy to get along with. Today we're supposed to be having all these nice little dialogues and futzing around with just about every kind of perfidious know-nothing alive, as if people were filled with good intentions. A plague on all this unity and equity dribble! What we need are priests with fortitude like Monsignor McGuiness. He knew how to handle those krauts from St. Cunegonde's across town; after they fought with their pastor and wanted to join a decent parish, he made them bring their own pews from their parish church and segregated them in the choir loft.

Yes, he could be irascible at times, especially with the altar boys. He was a no-nonsense man. We had to memorize our Latin forward and backwards, but today everything has to be in English.

International illiteracy! If you ask me, people are just too lazy to take the time to learn another language. I studied it for eight years and know it's not an easy language; but it helps a person build his vocabulary, and has such elegant and mellifluous qualities. It has a way of taking you away from everything, sort of into a respectable vacuum with God. Oh, yes, I know God doesn't talk in Latin, but He doesn't talk in English either. Now, don't get me wrong; I don't mind objections, not at all. To be perfectly frank, my ability in Latin is not very extensive, but it comes out of my mouth like soft butter when I read it to the people. And in the long run, it's considerably faster.

Which brings up another problem—all these young priests wanting to get married. It's downright indecent! They think they can solve all the world's problems by taking on a woman and spawning a batch of kids. I say, give them saltpeter. If they want to procreate, let them go out and raise some money for a school or parish hall, like we did, and have their names in brick and mortar. Monsignor McGuiness built one of the finest educational monuments you'd ever want to lay eyes on. A great deal of good it did, though; now the nuns want to close it down so they can run around in the slums dressed up like a bevy of cheerleaders. For sixty-one years Sister Boleslaus wore her starched wimple and never set foot inside a warm home. Sure, she was uncomfortable wearing all that gear and tackle. Who wouldn't be? My God, she wore enough material to start a dry goods store, but at least you knew she was a nun by the way she dressed. She wasn't out mincing around in her pumps like these gadflies you see nowadays. She stayed in the classroom, right until her dying day, teaching those innocent little children about the evils in the world. Mark my word, some of these religious orders will just phase themselves out of existence, mixing with lay people and parish trash. Why, just the other day one of them told me she no longer accepts clerical discounts, and I said, "Well, why should you? You don't *look* like a nun." Yes, they'll go modern all right, but they'll go bankrupt too.

As I was saying, these young priests don't know what's good

for them. During the depression I didn't worry a single day about my meals. People knew how to share with me. And during the war years I always had good cigarettes, not those off-brand things other people were smoking. And what's wrong with sleeping alone? I've been doing it for years and never became selfish or maladjusted. I'm no prude about the blisses of the married state, understand, but I'm smart enough to know when I'm well-off. I just have to laugh to myself when I hear about this loss of masculinity. I watch almost every baseball and football game that's televised. There aren't many other professional men who can match that! The trouble with the younger priests is that they not only have grown soft, they also have their minds in the gutter.

To top it off, they're even putting the liturgy right where their minds are—in the gutter. Can you imagine singing a Requiem High Mass with someone plunking away on his ukulele in the choir loft? I sneaked into one of those "happenings" the other day and watched them all get friendly, singing and shaking hands like they really enjoyed being with each other. It was disgraceful! I'd wager you my sterling silver St. Christopher's medal that you couldn't find a rosary in the whole lot. To me it looked more like a picnic or family reunion than it did a Mass. Personally, I was never one of those novena men with long lines of confessions afterwards, but I soon will be if these gypsies don't stop tampering with divine services. As a priest, I demand a little privacy when I offer Mass.

Speaking of privacy, what do you think of all this birth-control propaganda? You know as well as I do that it's Communist inspired, just like all the other problems we're confronting today. Blow the devils off the map! Then maybe we can settle back to some peaceful and charitable living again. Everyone knows the commies are in the government, but I think they're even getting to the Pope. All this demythologizing he's permitting those so-called biblical scholars—theological whippersnappers—to write and talk about. God just wouldn't play those kinds of tricks on us. I'm still a man of faith, but all this stuff isn't good for the

uneducated faithful to be reading. These ignoble hack writers—
no seminary training at all—just create a lot of news and stir
up people to get a little excitement started. Last Sunday I told
the people that if they didn't know what's what any longer, they
should stop by the rectory. I'm no oracle but, by God, I know
what's what.

To conclude, for the record, I'd like to say that all standards
and values have deteriorated—just gone *poof!* Honest to God,
I'm happy that dedicated souls like Sister Mary Boleslaus and
Monsignor McGuiness aren't around to see what has happened
to all their work. No one has any respect for the nice quiet things
they held so dear. They'd turn over in their graves if they could
see how the layman has his foot in every convent and rectory
door. They had a genuine contempt, and rightly so, for people
without authority, people who don't know their place. Indeed,
people have always been strange and stubborn and heretical, but
this present generation is simply frightening. We're living in horrendous times, and I for one make one last plea for the glorious
traditions of Sister Mary Boleslaus and Monsignor McGuiness,
lest we have to say *Sic transit gloria mundit* or something like that.

25. *FATHER CUSTER TAKES A STAND**

by Joel Wells

I GUESS SOME of you have been wondering when I would get around to talking about the new encyclical on birth control. Well, actually, it's not *just* about birth control. It's called *Humanae Vitae*—"Of Human Life"—and that's a big subject, a very big subject indeed. We could talk about the positive aspects of human life for a long time and not even begin to make a dent in the subject. The Pope stresses the dignity of life and the need to protect it from the insidious encroachments of materialism and hedonism and things like that. And the sanctity of marriage. There are lots of forces militating against that, you can be sure. . . .

Now the Bishop has asked that we all read this encyclical and form our consciences accordingly. You all heard Monsignor Doughty read the Bishop's letter last week. Well the Bishop also sent word that there was to be a sermon preached on the subject today in every parish and I guess this is it. It's a shame that Monsignor Doughty couldn't give it himself, being the pastor and all. But as you all . . . well, I mean . . . he's under the weather.

Some of you have called to say that you weren't altogether happy with the encyclical or with the Bishop's letter. But then

* From the September 15, 1968, issue of *Overview*.

some others called to say that it was about time and where did I think it left me after all my talk. . . . It seems I've taken on a sort of liberal image around here which isn't altogether justified in spite of some of the things I've preached about in the past . . . family limitation and celibacy. But I don't think I was ever really *for* birth control. I believed in what the Council called "responsible parenthood" and that in some circumstances this might work itself down to limiting—for serious reasons, of course, that's always understood—to limiting the number of children in a family. And then, of course, some people claim that rhythm didn't work very well for them and asked me if it wouldn't be all right if they took the pill for a while.

Well, as you may recall, there was a lot of talk about freedom of conscience then—right after the Council, I mean—and I may have gotten a little carried away and told a few people that it *seemed* to me that it *might* be a matter for them to decide individually, with the advice of their doctor, of course. But I want to make it perfectly clear that I never went around telling people that they should use the pill. You've got to remember that there was—there seemed to be—some question of doubt then. The theologicans talked a lot about that; practically every magazine and paper carried articles to that effect—that there was doubt and while there was doubt people were free to follow their own consciences. Why, some of those same theologians still seem to think that there's considerable room . . . some leeway . . . but. . . .

The thing is that the Pope has spoken now and the Bishop has spoken and Monsignor Doughty has spoken and . . . well, then there's the natural law as plain as the nose on your face and tradition besides that. It's not infallible, though. Even Rome admits . . . I mean, very few things we believe as Catholics have actually been pronounced *ex cathedra*, 100 percent infallible. But we believe them just the same, don't we? It would certainly take somebody with a great deal of pride to set themselves up as knowing more than the Pope, the Holy Father, especially in matters of faith and morals. You'd have to be awfully sure of yourself to do a thing like that. Not many people would dream of doing such a thing . . . well there was Martin Luther—people like that.

And you can be sure that the Holy Father didn't just sit down and dash this encyclical off. No. He agonized over the question for years and if you'll go to the trouble to read *Humanae Vitae* for yourselves and not go by what *Time* magazine and some of these progressive . . . radical . . . Catholic papers tell you you should be thinking about it—if you do that, you'll be able to see that the Holy Father went into every conceivable . . . I mean imaginable . . . aspect of it. He wasn't writing it just to spoil everybody's fun . . . I mean the joys of exercising your conjugal rights. Which is what some of these secular and radical papers would have you believe.

No. It would have been a lot easier for the Pope . . . the Holy Father to give in to all this popular pressure. But it's not his job to win popularity contests. He looked at all the facts and prayed over them and made his decision. He shut himself off from the world . . . well, not in that sense exactly. He felt it was too big . . . too complex . . . too delicate a problem to be dealt with effectively by the Vatican Council. There were hundreds of bishops there, speaking all sorts of languages and it would have taken them forever to arrive at a consensus. Then he set up a special commission composed of experts—doctors, theologians, Cardinals, even lay people—to study the question and give him their *opinion.* Even they couldn't reach a unanimous decision, some of them anyway . . . I mean a majority is not unanimity, not by a long shot. So it was left to the Holy Father to decide and he did.

Well, that's about all. I guess it's pretty clear where I stand. I know that most of you will take this in your stride. It's never been easy to be a Catholic. Nobody ever told us it would be easy, did they? But if there are still some who find it hard to accept . . . nobody expects you to take this lying down . . . er . . . but don't do anything rash. It can all be worked out with your confessor. Nobody's going to consign you to the fire and brimstone. Come to me and we'll talk it over in private. It would be better if you

came to me, I mean. Monsignor Doughty doesn't hear many confessions these days anyway because what with the overcrowding
of the school and all he doesn't have much time . . . anyway it
would be best if you saw me. I mean I didn't expect this any more
than . . . there's a faint possibility that . . . of . . . but it really
. . . oh, well. . . . Amen.